Beautiful, sensitive nature writing coupled with sound scientific observation, THE RUN is a chronicle of the annual migration of the alewife, from the ocean inland to the streams and ponds where they were spawned.

"This book mirrors an attempt to go farther afield, from one man's center. Its writing represents a kind of migration in itself. We all undertake them, whether we like it or not, near or far. To follow on the track of fish, birds, or any other animals, might be both discovery and repetition, because it might mean to go exhaustively into the nature of being alive. The alewives helped to open the world for me, although the outcome of their circling was always beyond knowing.

"Above all this book is about one race which has an equal status with us in the great motions of this planet. Men may be highest, or so men say, but they cannot be complete without granting equal dignity to the unsurpassed uniquesness of other forms of life. One ought to be able to say: 'Here is a life not mine. I an enriched.' "

From the *Preface*

THE RUN

John Hay

Illustrated by

David Grose

BALLANTINE BOOKS • NEW YORK
An Intext Publisher

Copyright © 1959 by John Hay

Library of Congress Catalog Card Number: 59-11598

SBN 345-02256-4-095

First Printing: August, 1971

Cover art by Murray Tinkleman

Printed in the United States of America

BALLANTINE BOOKS, INC.
101 Fifth Avenue, New York, N.Y. 10003

To my father and mother:
Clarence Leonard Hay
and
Alice Appleton Hay

CONTENTS

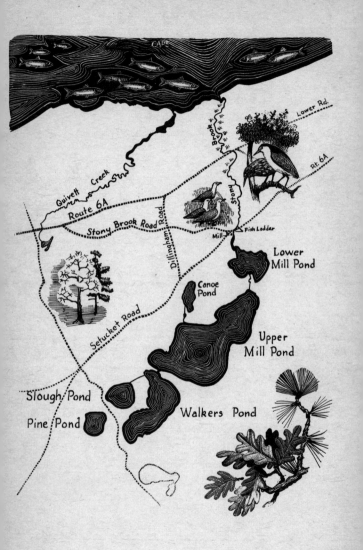

FOREWORD

This book mirrors an attempt to go farther afield, from one man's center. Its writing represented a kind of migration in itself. We all undertake them, whether we like it or not, near or far. To follow on the track of fish, birds, or any other animals, might be both discovery and repetition, because it might mean to go exhaustively into the nature of being alive. The alewives helped to open the world for me, although the outcome of their circling was always beyond knowing.

The Run

Above all this book is about one race which has an equal status with us in the great motions of this planet. Men may be highest, or so men say, but they cannot be complete without granting equal dignity to the unsurpassed uniqueness of other forms of life. One ought to be able to say: "Here is a life not mine. I am enriched."

Not a great deal has been written specifically about alewives, but the three published works I found most useful as an introduction were: *Fishes of the Gulf of Maine*, by Bigelow and Schroeder, published by the U.S. Fish and Wildlife Service; *A Report on the Alewife Fisheries of Massachusetts*, by David Belding, published by the Massachusetts Department of Conservation in 1921; and *Factors Influencing the Migration of Anadromous Fishes*, by Gerald Collins, Fishery Bulletin No. 73 of the Fish and Wildlife Service. I also received some helpful information from the Fisheries Research Board of Canada; and the Department of Sea and Shore Fisheries of the State of Maine, as well as its Department of Inland Fisheries and Game. Maine has been undertaking an important research and educational program with a view to rehabilitating the alewife fisheries.

I am greatly indebted to Hal Turner of Woods Hole, Dr. David Belding of Welfleet, and John Burns of the Massachusetts Department of Natural Resources, Division of Marine Fisheries, for answering my questions so readily and courteously; and of course, much thanks to Harry Alexander. He guards a good run.

THE RUN

I
WAITING THE WEATHER

It was in March, in comparative ignorance about their lives and habits, that I started looking for the alewives. This is the time of year when a few forerunners usually come in from the sea, in spite of the cold airs and waters that still grip the narrow land of Cape Cod. I had seen these migrant fish before, during a previous season, but from the road, so to speak. I had never followed them as if they challenged communication.

The place I started from was the Herring Run in the town of Brewster, part of a little migratory inland route by which the alewives travel up from

Cape Cod Bay to the inland ponds where they spawn. At the Herring Run the waters of Stony Brook pour down from an outlet north of these ponds—three of them, all interconnected: Walker's, Upper Mill, and Lower Mill. The flow then goes over a one-and-a-half-mile stretch, first over the fishway, a series of concrete ladders and resting pools built through rocks and high land, the area of the Herring Run, then through a valley of abandoned cranberry bogs bounded by low hills; and finally it elbows through tidal marshes to Paine's Creek, its mouth on Cape Cod Bay. This little river was called Sauquatuckett by the Indians and was subsequently known as the Setuckett River, Mill Brook, and Winslow's Brook. At its falling headwaters the first water mill in this region was built, and one of the later mill buildings is still standing—it has an old water wheel that is still in working order and is used to grind corn as a tourist attraction. By the time the mass of tourists arrive the alewife migration, aside from the "fry," hatched in the ponds and returning to salt water, has about run its course. They can still take pictures of the old mill in July or August, but they have probably missed a more vital antiquity.

The initial facts about the migration are these: each year, close in time to the vernal equinox when the sun crosses the equator and day and night are of equal lengths, this member of the herring family begins to enter innumerable inlets and tidal estuaries down the length of the Atlantic coast, from Newfoundland to the Carolinas. Scientifically known as *Pomolobus pseudoharengus* (also, under an older classification, *Alosa pseudoharengus*, along with species of shad), the alewife is an "anad-

2

romous" fish, meaning that like the salmon and shad, but unlike its relative the sea herring, it grows in salt water but leaves it as a three- or four-year-old adult, to spawn in fresh. A "catadromous" fish, like the eel, does just the opposite, growing up in fresh water and spawning in the sea.

The alewives, I learned, were due to come in from the Bay when the temperature of the brackish water that flowed into it was warmer than that of the salt water. In fact, a local resident had already noticed a group of eight or ten alewives of apparently large size that had appeared in the brook a few days before. Their arrival was a token that the land, though still cold, was warming up more quickly than the sea—just about the time a few male red-winged blackbirds showed up too, in advance of housekeeping. But if some began their migration in March, the first big run was not likely to come until the middle of April or later, depending on how long and cold a winter it had been. During an exceptionally cold season the alewives might not appear in volume until the first days in May. Where were they now, and what were they doing? Schooling somewhere offshore, and waiting to move in?

I stood on the beach and the sea still looked and felt and smelled as raw and cold as winter—iron-gray, massive, keeping its counsels—although, as I understood it in an incomplete way, the waters were undergoing seasonal adjustments at varying depths in the shallow coastal areas. Spring changes would begin to take effect. Perhaps I knew them, smelled them, on the sea wind. I was impatient. I wondered what specific combination of length of life, biological responses, currents, tides, the composition of the sea water, might impel one roving school of fish to leave the sea and start inland.

March, that season of the whole air hesitating and blowing back and forth, the circuit of the compass, especially in low-wooded seaside lands, is a time of hesitation, preparation, and violence. It is waiting weather.

The tempo had changed—it was late in February I had felt it. The winter fist began to unclench a little. Before another day of frost, sleet, or wet snow, spring rain might bucket down in the evening, or freak lightning might crack the sky. The days were gray and raw more often than not, but when the sun shone it was sheer grace. One night there were wands of light shuddering against great, shimmering, flushed curtains on the sky wall over Cape Cod Bay—being the legendary northern lights, grandly named aurora borealis. The following day was cold, dull, and obdurate again.

Then when the temperature began to ease up occasionally from the thirties to the forties, as March went on, a surprise snowstorm came howling in. Poles snapped; wires broke, and the resulting power failures lasted for several days, during which some people rediscovered fate. The radio, before communication was entirely cut, sounded off about the inexorable as cars and trains were stopped and men died after shoveling snow. In that whole weather always cast beyond complaint or prediction, this storm only represented a temporary arrest. Our primal agent the sun still had the season's growth in hand, more various than fate; which is not to minimize the tragedies along the way. Some days after the storm I found four or five male bluebirds in spring plumage all huddled dead in the bottom of a birdhouse—a pathetic brilliance. The entrance had probably been blocked by wet snow after they had taken refuge there.

As the growing sunlight played a steady tune, so the alewives, perhaps less affected by local storms than we, were due to come in, if only in small numbers. Where were they? I stopped by the Herring Run where the brook was full of loud cold water, but empty of fish. All the same, Harry Alexander, the alewife warden, was there, giving a display of public confidence. He had taken up his annual stance on Stony Brook Road, which bridges the run, and with a truculent punch of his lips against his pipestem, he made ready for the coming season.

In a world era, this is a local man. He has the cast and sense of place about him and some of its accumulated age. I have seen it in other men who have spent their lives in the same country environment. He is heavy, ruddy, thickset—an old boat in a Cape port. During his tenure on the alewives committee he seems to have developed a proprietary attitude about the run which probably exceeds his authority, but very few people object.

He certainly makes more of the job than the small wages he gets from the town; and in years past the alewives have had a defender in him at Town Meeting, when discussion came up about the amount of money allotted to the Herring Brook. From a naturalist's point of view, he can hardly be said to have much sentiment in him about these fish as part of the living community. Too many of them would stink the place up, or so he affirms.

The Run

I remember him at a hearing, speaking to a public official in this wise, "Ever see my brook? Our brook, I mean. No dirty, stinking mess up there!"

So, in his special way, he keeps the area clean, and is the herring's defender and interpreter. I think he likes to conceive of himself as a kind of rascal. To those who ask him about the fish he is liable to dispense information that is an outrage to the innocent. Two Connecticut schoolteachers were once directed to the run, and came away saying the alewives were often so plentiful that the Cape Codders shingled their houses with them. (This is part of what he has called "My fight with the public.")

So, a "Cape Cod character," personification of an old locality . . . but I don't think he would like me to write too well of his character. That day as I lingered at the run he gave me a lowering look. What was I interested in the fish for? Well, if I'd take the information from him, we could make ourselves a pile of money by selling the story to *Collier*'s magazine. Did I ever hear about the Indians shooting these fish from the trees?

Facts, Harry. Facts.

"Well, naow, I'll tell you. With the shore wind blowing on the long flats out there and the water ruffling up like that, the fish don't come in much. But they'll be along. Yes-yes."

So was there nothing to do but take tentative steps and wait? The scene, the place, the weather —an emergent weather in me perhaps—was more compelling than that. The wind blowing, brook roaring, sun shafts through the steely sky, all urged an opening. I walked down to the south side of the road, by the tall lilacs, under high willows and maple trees. Here the waters of the brook divide between the concrete fishway and a side or "waste" stream which rejoins the other some fifty feet farther on, dropping precipitously over rocks that foam with water too high for the migrating fish to leap.

I walked down a path at the edge of this narrow waste stream. Where the water was running swiftly, lithely, between the high rock foundations of the road on one side and a low dirt bank with grass hummocks on the other, I saw the brown head of a muskrat leading across the stream not more than twenty feet away. The sleek, dark little animal swam over to a stone across from me and sat there eating something with quick, legerdemain little gestures, a fast shuttling between its paws and its whiskered face. Apparently it couldn't see me. The east wind was blowing across us, and the fresh waters were roaring. Then it stopped and nosed back into the stream, swimming across to a tussock not more than twelve feet from where I stood. It plucked out, quickly, a sizable bunch of grass and swam back with it to the same eating place and chewed it up. Then it returned to the shallow water, swimming close to the bottom, where I could plainly see it going easily against the current with its two hind legs stretched out, propelling it, and the long flat tail acting as a scull.

It emerged to disappear in a few rock crevices and then came out, its glossy, questioning head sniffing for danger before it dropped down again. Finally it swam out of sight into the cruel brilliance of sunreflecting waters that ran full out, full tilt. Pools of plenty were continually releasing and boiling as if they were the strength and source of all motion.

The muskrat's eyes were black as rock recesses

and its pelt as dark and glistening as a mud bank. It was at home, with all its food around it—grass, minnows, salamanders, fresh-water mussels—in an adaptation, a closeness to the place, arrived at through both random and inevitable forces. It knew its small world and needed no outside instruments to set its course by. I might wonder about the next event, the coming storms, but here was this animal swimming away as if it said, "Come on in. The universal water's fine."—in a stream as yet too cold for me.

II
ARRIVAL

A week or so later, early in April, I finally saw my first alewife of the season. It had the brook to itself where I caught sight of it—a cloudy form running upcurrent—and when I went closer I could see it probing the rippling, beating waters, with all that fish articulation of separate fins together, fanning slightly, waving, threading, and steering, the fixed eyes staring on, its whole body weaving with the flow. It is a surprisingly large fish, seen for the first time in a narrow stream. Its length may be anywhere between ten and thirteen inches, and it has a heavy look for those who are used to sunfish and minnows.

The Run

An alewife was no novelty to me, but this one seemed to decide the year's direction. It started things out. I saw it for the first time, as child or genius does who finds some whole deep image in the air, or radiant clarity in the water. I had the feeling too that I was looking at a professional from an old water world, a new agent of old assurance, deserving profound respect. After all, it had been coming back here thousands of years before me, in the migrant history of its race, and by this time must have mastered its passage. And as a natural event, a part of the spring's development, it seemed to announce that bud scales on shrubs and trees would start to crack and fall away to let the inner shoots out that unfold as leaves and feed on the sun. It said that flies and wasps and spiders would come out of winter hiding and sleeping, that the song sparrows would begin to sing in the willows and viburnum bushes along the banks of Stony Brook.

There is something exciting and strange about the sudden appearance of new life in the spring, coming from another region, another climate. The terns or plovers that appear along the shore bring an unknown experience with them. They seem to start in or to assemble according to some tremendous demand which is in no way restricted to seasonal lags. They recur; they are recognizable; and yet they bring in endless tides and vivid journeys, being a part of that remarkable projection of nature in which a multitude of lives use their skill in navigation, their plumage, their scales, fins, and various senses, their particular drives toward fulfillment.

Migration is universal. That which prompts animals to emerge from their burrows, or to start moving over the ocean floor, to fly north, to swim into brackish or fresh water from salt, or even, like a ladybird beetle, to move a short distance from a forest floor to a meadow, must have a world-wide energy to it, with lines of communication that reach everywhere ahead and invite the human drive for knowledge. But in a strict sense there are two accepted definitions of migration for the animals. There is return migration, of which the alewives provide an example. Fish or birds in this category travel seasonally from one area to another, usually coming back to some home region after varying lapses of time. Otherwise, there is emigration, in which animals leave their home base but never come back again, lemmings and locusts being good examples. Both definitions, I should think, can prove that home stretches farther than we know.

Why had this pioneer of an alewife, and the others that had come before it, arrived so soon? It is possible that they had migrated up Stony Brook before. All mature alewives—a majority seem to be four years old—are moved by sexual development and swim inshore when the temperature of the fresh or brackish water has turned warmer than the salt water from whence they came. The earliest comers often appear to be larger in size. This suggests, at least, that they may be older and that they have spawned in that run before. The latest to come seem to be the smallest, and therefore the youngest. Alewives, like other fish, seem to have a tendency to keep growing, though there may be a maximum size reached in their fifth or sixth year. The only conclusive way to tell their age is by microscopic examination of their scales, which reflect each spawning year and its physical changes.

Work done by Keith Havey on alewives in

Maine shows a minimum of alewives spawning at three years of age and the largest number in the four- or five-year-old range. No scales were found which reflected more than two spawnings. As to size, he gives a sampling of their length in inches which graduates up from 11.25 inches in the three-year-old fish to 11.80 in the four-year-olds, 12.35 in the five-year-olds, and 12.80 in the six. The female alewife, incidentally, is a little larger than the male.

Possibly then, these early alewives at Stony Brook were the oldest, and because of that they might have been the most practiced at finding their way. I am told that, with new fish ladders, observers have noticed the earliest arrivals seeking and passing through them more readily on the second year after construction than on the first, which leads to the belief that they have been through before. Age may improve the alewife in prowess, though it is a fish of crowds, and not one to strike out much on its own. The "homing instinct," still unfathomed, but about which I will try to say more later on, brings them back to their streams of origin with almost united force.

So my lone alewife marked the greatness it preceded, though it was early, in early and still undecided weather. At first the sleet, hail, flurries of wet snow came in profusion, stabbing between the sunshine, as though nature, before making its next terms known, was full of passionate unease. Then wings of warm rain would beat in over the Cape, to slash and curve and follow along trees and houses, through inland ponds, across the ridges and hollows, and the wind poured behind in great gusts, trying, it seemed, to shake a tight

world loose. Underneath the struggling air many things waited for more chances in the sun, but under the stars, on foggy evenings or bright days, the singing of peepers in pools, ponds, or boggy land would swell and widen everywhere.

Then as the month kept advancing, that which came out began to stay, and to expand, in variety, flexibility, and strength. The wheels of the world seemed to turn more brightly. I felt a suggestion in each changing tree, in the loosening ground, the kinetic light and air, of new unfoldings, kaleidoscopic discoveries. The formality and power in the coming on of spring surprised me, as if it had never come before.

More winds began to blow from the southwest, the prevailing wind during late spring and summer. Yellow fingertips of bloom showed on the whip-long branches of the forsythias. The temperature edged toward the fifties, and there were deep new meetings between the moles and the worms. One day many tree swallows began to flit and dive low around the Herring Run. They skimmed along the surface of the water, then sailed up again. Their bellies were as white as a frog's or horned pout's, dark wings and tails trimly cut, backs almost a tropical blue in the light above the water, reflecting green at some angles, or a green-blue-purple the color of mackerel. Their flight dipped with the up and down flying insects they were chasing. When some insect, unseen to me, spiraled straight up along the banks, a swallow would leave its water gliding, twist suddenly, beating its wings, and almost spiral after.

That original source of energy the sun, which men might still worship in good faith, was bringing out new facets to shine abroad. The web of life was stretching to its light. Birds, insects, plants, and fish were beginning to move to its changing measure; though if some days were warm with a budding, fringing, easing expectation, others were still raw, wet, and contracting, bringing winter back to flesh and fiber. We kept looking for the alewives. Cars would slow up at the Herring Run. The drivers peered down to see the curving, dark forms of a few fish holding up against the current. Then they drove on. Or they got out, saw nothing, and went away in disappointment. But suddenly one morning toward the middle of April the crowd of alewives had so increased as to cause an inescapable excitement in the vicinity. The water was thick with fish, their fins showing on the surface. It was almost as it had been a hundred years before when the whole population would cry out at their coming, "The herring are running!"

III
DRIED FISH: AN INFORMAL HISTORY

"The herring are running!" must have been a great cry once, for men, women, and children over the whole Cape. There was a deep meaning in this seasonal event, since the fish were a part of the local livelihood the year around. Nowadays, so far as commerce is concerned, the alewives lack their former importance. In Massachusetts, although they come into a number of streams and rivers few alewives are taken for the market. I understand that in recent years only the runs at Brewster and Middleboro have been open for commercial use, the fishing rights having been sold to the highest bidder.

For all that, it still seems a live, high, and social morning when you wake to the gabbling of gulls in the distance and know that the alewives have finally arrived. The sun spreads down new warmth. There are cool sweeps of breeze, broad runs of blue in sky and sea past the gray and white houses, with those silver hordes starting to enter inland veins in a bold reminder of perpetuity.

This season the rights to fish the stream had been bought from the town by a firm that wanted them for lobster bait. On the eighteenth day of the month a big red truck had pulled alongside the seining pool and the old mill. Three men were down in the pool, with their rubber boots on, putting a wide net in place. It was rimmed with cork floats and roped at the center to a hoist fixed to a small dock on the bank. A little wire gate was closed at the stream entrance on the upper side of the pool, so that the fish could go no farther. The run was officially on; and until it thinned out two months ahead, the fish would be hauled from the pool four days a week, thrown into barrels, and trucked away to be sold as lobster bait.

A sign was posted at Stony Brook, reading: "No herring may be taken or molested in Stony Brook on Fridays, Saturdays, and Sundays in accordance with state law. Residents of Brewster are entitled without charge to one dozen herring daily on Mondays, Tuesdays, Wednesdays, and Thursdays during the open season, and should obtain them from J. B. Salvadore, Jr., who has purchased the Herring Fishery Rights for this year, or may take them from the brook on these days if he is not present." It was signed by the selectmen of the town of Brewster.

On the down side of the road a bunch of children were celebrating the coming of the fish. The alewives, crowding, resting, circling, and slipping up through the pools and falls of the fishway—their bodies a fretted-lavender brown in the bubbling waters—were now fair game for the inland world they had come back to. Three boys were competing for a crab net they were dipping into the water, scooping after the fish, and as often as not heaving it up empty. One of them was professionally pinching the belly sides of a fat, gleaming alewife to see if it was a female and would emit some of its roe. Then he flung it back into the water with furious energy; and it slapped hard when it hit, and he cheered.

Were they under the law, these predators? Well, this play, or hunt, this spring jubilation had been going on for several hundred years.

"Let the kids play around there, I say," said Herring Harry. "We were kids too. We didn't start out old."

In barer, colder, perhaps simpler days, days when men lived closer to their natural surroundings and were more dependent on them than they think they are now, the alewives meant food and revenue, an abundance returning to your own back yard. They came under the heading of useful acquaintances. But now the roe, or fish eggs, is the only part of the alewife that is highly considered locally. It is a very bony fish and most people reject the idea of eating it, forgetting the days of "good salt herring" when the children ate them on sticks like candy. So the Brewster resident gets his allotment for the roe, to be fried in butter. An ambitious gardener can bury the rest under his corn plantings to serve as fertilizer, if the cats permit, though it is still a very good way to make corn grow tall in unreceptive soil. A hundred years ago or more, when it was done extensively, it resulted in rich yields. I have heard that one acre set with a thousand fish would produce three times as much corn as an acre without them. It is a practice that we inherit from the Indians, although the Indian agriculturist was likely to be plagued by wolves instead of cats.

Cape Codders, even so comparatively short a time ago as fifty or sixty years, would not have liked to hear this farming method belittled. Some of them may even have regarded it with delight. I recently talked with a man who was a boy in the 1890's and remembers walking behind a wagonload of "very dead" fish in a field made ready for corn. A man in the wagon pitched out a forkful of herring into each prepared hole as they creaked along, while another, walking behind, shoved dirt over them and planted the seed. He can remember a relative cocking a keen ear one night and saying, "Listen! You can hear it growing. By God, when their feet hit that stinking mess don't they start up and go!"

Although to know them may have been to understand their worth, I find one early writer, Marshall McDonald Douglass, in his *North America*, 1740, who does not give the tribe much credit. "Alewives," he says, "by some of the country people are called Herrings. They are of the Herring tribe but much larger than the true Herring. They are a very mean, dry and insipid fish. Some of them are cured in the manner of white Herrings and sent to the sugar islands for the slaves, but because of their bad quality they are not in request: in some places they are used to manure the land. They are very plenty, and come up the rivers and brooks into ponds in the spring." None the less, they used to be smoked or pickled in brine and shipped out in barrels to the West Indies, and whether or not the quality was bad the demand was enough to make the trade in them into one of great volume, part in fact of the famous swap for molasses, later turned into New England rum, which was so important in our early history.

Before I try to defend these fish against any further imputations, I should explain their name. "Herrin'" is the name and pronunciation on Cape Cod. I don't call them alewives just to defy such Cape Codders as might be fussy about it, but to differentiate them from their more famous cousins the sea herring, which spawn in salt water. Cape Cod has its alewives committees, and it may be that the fish were called alewives here before they were called herrin'.

You can still read statements to the effect that the original name "alewife" is a corruption of the Indian word "aloofe," which meant bony fish. In 1871 a gentleman named J. Hammond Trumbull tried to scotch this bit of etymology by pointing out —in a government publication on Sea Fisheries, that the Narragansett and Massachusetts Indians called the alewife and herring "Aumsu-og," as had been noted by Roger Williams. In any case, whichever Indianism we choose, it seems more likely that the name stemmed from English dialect. "Allizes," not at all like aloofe, was one of the names applied to it in company with the allice shad. To quote Mr. Trumbull again: "The modern English 'allis' was in old French and old English 'alouze' or 'aloose,' nearer than the modern form of the name to the Latin 'alausa.'" The latest in this chain of spellings is of course *Alosa*, the scientific handle now applied to the shad, and in some texts to the alewife.

To the English colonists an alewife was also an alehouse keeper. *A Dictionary of Americanisms* quotes a volume printed in 1675 which said: "The alewife is like a herrin', but it has a bigger bellie, therefore called an alewife." (Let that quotation be of some comfort to the proponents of herrin'. The name has a formal heritage.) The writer was surely not making a direct physical analogy between a woman and a fish. The original alewife he probably has reference to is a shad, but *Pomolobus pseudoharengus* does have a deep body and is heavily built forward, so perhaps a comparison with a hearty alewife of sixteenth- or seventeenth-century England would not be too far-fetched.

The poet Skelton described an alewife, Eleanor Rummying by name, who lived in the time of Henry VIII. She brewed a "hoppy ale," and "her face was wondrously wrinkled, lyke a rost pigges eare bristled with here"—at which point I will let the analogy go on its merry way.

The alewife has had a variety of local and common names, the kind that indicate touch and sight, the handing on of natural meetings—the signposts of its contacts with man and his history on the eastern shores of this continent. It is known as "sawbelly," for example, referring to the fine sharp little notches or teeth on the midline of its belly; and for the large eyes, set on each side of its small head, it has been called "wall-eyed herring," "big-eyed herring," or "blear-eyed herring." It is also the "spring herring," "branch herring," "river herring," or "fresh-water herring."

This old New England name of alewife has its modifications in "Ellwife" and "Ellwhop" on the Connecticut River, and there were variant pronunciations in other regions. In the state of Rhode Island alewives were called "buckies" and in Maine "catthrashers." In Canada the name is "Gaspereau," sometimes "Gasparot." The term "alewife" is uncommon in the maritime provinces. There seem to be three Gaspereau Rivers, two in New Brunswick and one in Nova Scotia, in addition to a town of that name in New Brunswick, and a lake in Nova Scotia. Apparently the place name derives from the fish, and not the other way around. In its 15th Report, for 1917, the Geographic Board of Canada says "after a fish," in explaining the name of the Gaspereau River. Another Canadian term for alewife is "kyak" or "kyack," which sounds like a derivation from northern Indians. Mr. A. H. Leim of the Biological Station at St. Andrews, New Brunswick, writes me that he has only heard "one or two fishermen call them 'kyacks'; one of these was an old poacher on the Shubenacadie River in Nova Scotia who always used this name. I assume the word is of Indian origin."

Finally the alewife is called "grayback," a name that distinguishes it from a close relative often confused with it, which is called the "blackback," "blueback," or "glut herring" (*Pomolobus aestivalis*). The blueback shows up in a late spring run, and seems to spawn in the lower reaches of a stream, instead of migrating up to its headwaters. It has smaller eyes than the "grayback" and as its name indicates its back is dark blue, instead of greenish gray, but as colors fade at death, this is no sure test. The two species of alewife can only be told apart conclusively by dissection. The lining of the blueback's body cavity is black instead of pink or gray.

These names are also indicative of the range of the alewife, all the way from the Gulf of St. Lawrence to the Carolinas. In the spawning season they come inland by way of sandy inlets, great tidal bays, freshwater river mouths, or creeks only a few yards wide. Most of the streams by which they are still able to swim up have their local history of fishing alewives, either with traps, weirs, dip nets, or even pails. In the fisheries of Maine it is known as "alewife dipping." This is an important "food fish," even though it may never have approached the sea herring in numbers, nor been as famous as the cod.

If the English sailor, Captain Bartholomew Gosnold, had been ashore in the springtime instead of on his ship when he gave the Cape its name, it might now be called Cape Alewife.

Though they are only part of a multitude of other lives that nurtured the American past, the alewives should be given high and special credit. William Bradford's *Of Plymouth Plantation* testifies to their vital importance in the Pilgrims' first year. After the *Mayflower* left in early April of 1621, Squanto, that greatly helpful Indian, showed them "that in the middle of April they should have store enough come up the brook by which they began to build, and taught them how to take it, and where to get other provisions necessary for them." This brook ran, as it still runs, through the town, so that the Plymouth inhabitants were lucky to have their supply of alewives close at hand—they seemed to have depended on them primarily for plantings, also taught them by Squanto. The fish came in "fat and fair" and amazingly plentiful after a lean winter full of apprehension. At first apparently each inhabitant took freely of the fish in the brook, but this seems to have resulted in "injuring the property of those near the place of taking." As a result the Town Brook became town responsibility after a few years, and the fishing was regulated. The cost of a weir was distributed among the inhabitants and the fishing put under the charge of town officers, with fines set for taking alewives without permission. Innumerable fish laws were passed after that, from the Colony of Plymouth to the Commonwealth of Massachusetts. The fish ran comparatively free for a while, but through the progression of these laws you might watch, in town after town, the gradual growth of human population plus human concern for a valuable product. In 1709 a general law provides: "That no wears, hedges, fishgarths, stakes, kiddles, or other disturbance or encumbrance shall be set, erected or made, on or across any river, to the stopping, obstructing, or straitning of the natural or usual course and passage of the fish in their seasons, or spring of the year, without the approbation and allowance first had and obtained from the general sessions of the peace in the same county. . . ." An Act of 1741, to "Prevent the destruction of the fish called alewives, and other fish," might indicate that the colonists were beginning to notice a decline in their numbers and to be apprehensive about it, although it is hard to judge. *A History of Barnstable County*, published in 1890, has this to say: "Early in the last century the supply of herring so far exceeded the demand for fish food that the surplus was used to fertilize the fields, and the growing custom of using them in each hill of planted corn was checked in 1718, the town fathers [of Bourne] ordering that none should be taken in the future to 'fish corn' "

Apparently the alewife population did start to decrease a long time ago. Fishermen along the Merrimack River noticed a diminishing in numbers as early as the mid-eighteenth century; and somewhat later they thought it might be due to the number of small ponds which had been dammed up. These ponds had access to the river and so provided spawning grounds. Certainly the alewives, through man's agency, began to suffer great setbacks in the old use of their runs. Some of the first culprits were the woolen mills, and corn or grist mills such as the one at Brewster—they blocked up many of the runs, in spite of the fish laws. Then a tremendous industrial expansion put cities and factories along all big rivers and many large streams, adding more mill dams across the runs. The resulting sewage and manufacturing wastes polluted the waters, destroying many fish, and making some rivers completely unfit for migration. Extensive deforestation also resulted in the drying up of a number of streams and the lowering of water levels. The nineteenth century was a notorious plunderer.

Alewives in any large number now coincide with undeveloped areas, which happen to be comparatively few along the Atlantic coast. As a result of industrialization the original heavy runs were so reduced that the only important, commercial runs are now in the southern part of the alewife range, notably the Chesapeake, or north of Rhode Island. Although the fish still have much less access to their ancient, natural routes, the existing runs are probably less carelessly protected by law. State laws put the responsibility of keeping the fishways clear on the localities through which they run, but the state supervises their condition, and if a run is too depleted the state can forbid the sale of its fishing rights. Whatever may be said about their decline in the long run, it is quite likely that state supervision has helped to increase the alewife population during comparatively recent years. It certainly seems to be true that the number of fish at the Brewster run has increased since the fish ladders were built in 1945. The new fishways made the rocky, often clogged stream easier of access, and cut down on fish mortality as they ascended. They can, in other words, be brought back; although there are fishermen in Maine who estimate that the alewife population is only a third as large as it was some fifty years ago, and there are those who say the decline has been even greater in Massachusetts.

A great many of the old alewife fisheries lost their vitality because there was no longer any local dependence on them nor any general call for the product. A recent article in the *Maine Coast Fishermen* said this: "A few weeks ago in Wareham, Mass., the local selectmen refused to auction off the fishing rights, feeling the bids were too low. An old timer of the town, who has watched these migrations since he was a boy, recalled that the alewife rights to the stream in question once brought as much as $12,000 a year." In the smaller run at Brewster, incidentally, the bid taken during the last spawning season was $450.

Control is still local. Where there are still good-sized runs, the towns appoint alewives committees, whose members are re-elected annually at Town Meeting. In Brewster, on a salary of some twenty-five dollars a year, plus small wages for time spent, it is their job to keep the Herring Run area neat;

to post regulations; see that no individual gets away with more than his allotted portion of fish; and keep the stream free from obstruction so that the fish can proceed to their spawning grounds, as well as into the nets of the concessionaire. The town sells annual rights for the privilege of fishing the stream in season, four days a week. On the other days the alewives are allowed to go ahead and propagate their kind. The five hundred barrels or more of fish that have been taken yearly from Stony Brook happened to have been used recently for lobster bait.

To some extent, incidentally, their use and commercial value depends on their condition and flavor. An alewife's flesh is best when it has been taken directly out of salt water. The ocean flavor is progressively lost as the fish migrates through inland streams. So they have their highest value where the runs are located close to the sea, or tidal rivers such as the one at Damariscotta, Maine.

The West Indies trade is over, as well as the days of "good salt herring." The most likely place to see indications of alewife now is on the stupendously bountiful shelves of a chain store, in the form of a can with a picture of a cat on it. And the future of the alewife, in human hands at least, seems to depend on a wider demand for it. It is valued neither for sport nor edibility, but is used for cat and dog food, fish meal, and pickled fish, with some, as at Brewster, being taken for lobster bait. Apparently there is an innate prejudice among some New Englanders against using a traditional food fish for other purposes, and a belief that selling it for meal or cat food is less profitable. Put this down to thrift, or respect for old ways, still it stands against the fact that the alewife's latest value comes from its status as a processed, rather than edible, food. "Reduction" is what they call it when the alewives are turned into fish meal, and in a sense perhaps they have been reduced, at least in our personal esteem. They now belong to a technical age with the rest of us.

With modern methods of handling, packing, and transportation the old fisheries may have been left behind, but it should be said that, because of its new status in commerce, ignominious or not, the alewife may stand a better chance. The State of Maine, for example, has been undertaking thorough study of the alewives in order to find out how old runs can be brought back, or new ones created. They are a fish that are very responsive to management. When barriers are removed and open fishways are made, they take their opportunity.

All is not well with the traditional ways, though the alewives may be perfectly ready to go beyond them. In the old days on Cape Cod there was hardly a seafaring man who did not take his salt herring abroad with him, and on land, after being salted, dried in the sun, and smoked, they were strung on sticks and sold for ten cents a stick. There were many smokehouses on the Cape, and in the wintertime dried fish hung on the barn rafters above the haylofts. I have a comment on those days from Mr. Alexander: "None of your First National Stores then," said he. "We lived off the earth . . . potatoes and smoked herrin'. That's why some of us old goats lived so long."

It is hard to find smoked herring these days. It is a skill that seems to have almost gone; and I am told that there used to be a good deal of variation in the product. Smoked fish are now easier to find in Maine than on Cape Cod. I bought a pair recently in a small general store in Maine at the excessive price of fifteen cents. A dried alewife was handsomer than I had suspected, and the smell not unpleasant, although I might not say as much for a barnful. The head and eye sockets were encrusted with salt, and the hard thin body was colored a bronze and smoky gold as though heat still roamed the scales. I was reminded for some reason of a metal bowl I had once seen that came from the land of the Incas. I peeled off the scales and chawed a toast to our ancestors.

IV
THE
REPRODUCTIVE URGE

The fishing operation near the old grist mill was in full swing after the twenty-third of April. The *Salvadore* crew was hauling in their net with the aid of a winch. It was loaded with fish, enough to fill four or five barrels. The victims were flipping and flashing with a whirring violence, a high sound going up in the gray morning air, a beautiful iridescence in their white-silver sides. The whole dripping net was heavy and alive with their shivering, thrashing, and dying. Heads butted through the mesh and gills caught, in their frantic, vibrating despair . . . and all for lobster bait, worth six dollars a barrel.

The Run

The early colonists spoke of alewives coming up their streams in "incredible" numbers, and so it still looks, though Stony Brook, for one, is narrow in its upper reaches, and when the fish are forced into it they are crowded beyond all proportion. The inland stream, with its fresh-water grasses, insects, and small fish is suddenly host to a large and almost foreign form of life, except that they are both closely joined to the sea.

On the whole, it had been a rainy month. The brook below the seining pool was roaring and foaming down. Such was the teeming crowd of alewives trying to swim up through the ladder, through the violently heavy flow, that there was a constant falling back, a silver slapping and flapping over the concrete rims of the pools. Farther down, where the waste stream tumbled over a small mountain of rocks, too high for the fish to jump (their limit, on a vertical leap, seems to be not much over two feet), there was a scene to force the heart. Always a certain number of fish, dividing from those that swam the main stream toward the ladder, would attempt the impossible at this place. Ordinarily, when an alewife meets obstacles in its advance upcurrent it will quickly go forward into it, then leap in short dashes over rocks and the lip of fishways. I had seen them go up without apparent rest where the stream falls down the inclined ladder at the pond outlet above. They were dancing and flipping up those waters, which were rushing and bubbling down, like kites in a fast wind.

Yet here, for all their instinctive valiance, was the unsurmountable. Now, as they had done for thousands of years, they tried and failed. White tons of water smashed down over the rocks, but time and time again one fish after another made a

quick dash into it and almost flew, hanging with vibrant velocity in the torrent until it was flung back. Many were exhausted and found their way back to the main stream, circling and swimming slowly, and a large number were smashed against the rocks to turn belly up and die, eaten later by young eels, or gulls and herons, as they were taken downstream by the current. Some were wedged in the rocks and could be seen there for days as the water gradually tore them apart until they were nothing but white shreds of skin.

A wooden bridge crosses over Stony Brook at this point. A neighbor of mine, a mother of children, was standing there watching when I came up, and I heard her say, "Terrible!" I guessed that she knew what she saw, besides death and defeat. It was the drive to be, a common and terrible sending out, to which men are also bound in helplessness.

We are astonished by this fantastic drive. "What is the point? What makes them take these suicidal chances? Why?" It is as if we were trying to get back, or down, to an explanation in ourselves that we had lost sight of. But somewhere in us, through this feverish, undecided world, we still know.

Are they stupid? There is no measure in the world of nature more excellent than a fish. It may be comparatively low in the evolutionary scale of complexity, but no animal is more finely made, or better suited to its own medium. All the same, the unvaried blindness their action seemed to show would sometimes strike me as hard as did their ability in the water.

Stony Brook was black with them. There was no open patch of stream bed to be seen. And with the excessive crowding, the general procession, so steadily insistent on its own time, was hurried up to some extent. Their motion became almost ponderous and tense, while individual fish leaped like dolphins, pewter- and gold-sided, over and through the dark herd. Others circled in and out or kept pace with the rest, staring ahead.

They had a synchronized momentum of their own. If I dropped a stone in the middle of them, they would separate at that point and then close in to fill the gap. There could be no nullifying or breaking their united persistence. Their onwardness, their desperate dashing against the rocks, had its own logic—a logic which had nothing to do with hope, reason, or choosing another alternative. No way out, in other words. Slavery to the reproductive urge. These alewives are more dumb than sheep. If you were to press your own sympathy hard enough, you might feel a terrible lack of variety in them, or, paradoxically enough, of daring. The lidless-eyed and plunging multitude seems brutally driven, without a chance. This is "togetherness" with a terrible vengeance.

Perhaps there is something here that we know too, as fellow animals, and lose sight of. At the risk of making one of those vaguely anthropomorphic assumptions against which the objective scientists are constantly warning us, I would guess that the selfmotivation in this onward mass of fish might be compared to those human crowds that take action under stress, independently of the individuals that make them up. Suddenly a crowd, hitherto a random combination of people, takes on a frightening rhythm and purpose of its own. It is governed by laws which go back infinitely farther in the history of life than the immediate goal of its anger or exultation.

I have explained nothing. I can only say that when I first saw these fish I was moved in spite of myself. Instinct is no more blind than wonder. To have the human attributes of mind and spirit and the race's ability to control its own environment does not give me the wit to beat the infinitely various will of life at its own game. All I could wish for would be to join it.

I walked on down the banks of Stony Brook, past the Herring Run area with its neat paths, bridges, and fish ladders, my shoes squashing in the mud. The stream turns a slight angle at this point, gets broader and shallower and begins to run through the little valley that ends in tidal marshes and the Bay. The alewives, for a hundred yards at least, were running up against the downward currents, massed almost stationary, not in ranks, but ordered mutuality, with a long waving like water grasses or kelp, and curving, twisting, swirling like their medium the water as they moved very gradually ahead. There was no indiscriminate rushing ahead. It was done to measure; but it seemed to me that through their unalterable persistence I saw the heaving of crowds of all kinds, of buffalo, cattle, sheep, or men. I had seen as much motion in crowds pouring out of a subway entrance or massing through a square. History was in their coming on, without its shouts and cheers. They could not speak for themselves; but who knew how deep the silence went?

Ahead of them there was a net; behind, down the broader reaches of the brook, the greedy herring gulls dropped down into the water after them, or stood along the bank in apparently glutted satisfaction, while others screamed and sailed overhead. In spite of their slow gliders' grace and local lethargy compared with swift sea birds like the terns, gulls travel the rims of the world. They had always made me think of far-distance, voyages unending. Many of them had congregated on a bald hill that overlooks the run and were standing like white sentries under the shafts of the northern sky beyond. From far off they sometimes suggest rows of military crosses, and I have heard them compared to a field of flowers. Soldiers, flowers, graves . . . all these they might suggest on the heights of fate, by their pure bold greed and unmatched design. They stood on a wide stage.

V
THE NATURE
OF AN ALEWIFE

The fish kept moving up. I watched them swinging back and forth with the current, great-eyed, sinewy, probing, weaving, their dorsal fins cutting the surface, their ventral fins fanning, their tails flipping and sculling. In the thick, interbalanced crowd there would suddenly be a scattered dashing, coming as quickly as cat's-paws flicking the summer seas. They may have moved by "reflex" rather than conscious thought, but what marvelous professionals they were in that!

The cold raw winds of April had heeled back, and May swung on. There were an increasing number of days with the wind from the southwest, smelling of sunny springtime. The local paper had it that the temperature averaged a high of 66.6 degrees Fahrenheit and a low of 44.2 in the week between the second and the ninth of May. The following week the average rose a little, going to between 67.5 and 47 degrees. The first reported striped bass, a three-and-a-half-pounder, was caught on the Cape the eighth of the month.

The willows that hung over the Herring Run were budding and flowering out, lacing and fringing with many beads, a yellow-green; and leaves of the red maples began to unfold, a light coppery russet color, hanging like limp claws—and elsewhere, on higher ridges and other roads, the oaks in their leafy variety of pink, yellow, gray and pale green, were starting their fires with tenderness. Clouds of the shad-blow's lacy white blossoms came out everywhere between pitch pines and oaks, to last only a few days and be replaced by beach plums whose flowers burst out of their sheaths like popping corn.

The procession, down the brook and around its bend, made other rushing sounds above the noise of the flow itself. The gulls in the valley were crying out with "ho!" and "ha!" and "yi!" The shadow of a gull flying high over us fell across the water and the alewives rushed to the side. The backs of some of them were cruelly gashed. There was a dead one on the bank, stiff and dry, flatly reflecting the blue in the sky like an unpolished knife blade.

They were close-packed going up through the ladders, herding, slipping, slanting, struggling in relation to each other. I grabbed one out with my hands. It shuddered, was almost still for a second or two, like a man with his wind knocked out, then plunged in my hands and slipped out onto the bank. It thrashed there in the grass, a twelve-inch fish, with a gray-green back, and silver sides and belly that reflected the magnificent surfaces of May, with grass, sun, and blue sky intruding through the overhanging leaves and the brown earth. It shone with violet, yellow-green, white and brown, pink and blue. It had an inclusive majesty, a great natural art.

Its silver scales are large, like iridescent reflecting coins: and in the water the alewife is able to alter the pigmentation of its skin so as to blend with the background. It is able to do this very quickly, so that it changes in color as it moves up the stream to correspond with a darker or lighter bottom . . . part of the whole various pattern of adaptation which the fish show to the water around them.

During the course of evolution brain development among the fishes has been slow. What brain power they have is closely related to their sense organs, concentrated on their whole bodily co-ordination; in which, so far as water action is concerned, they are man's superiors. An alewife's body is marvelously fitted to situation—peace or turbulence, light or dark, flood and ebb, ripple or rile. This inhabitant of the sea weaves up through the overhanging springtime, and seems a part of it, experienced as to its flowering.

For it is a salt-water fish, as I sometimes had to remind myself later between the ponds and the Bay, although there is a landlocked variety; and as such it is part of a prodigious tribe. As a member of the herring family—the Clupeidae, it is related to the sea herring, sprats, shads, pilchards, and menhadens. The sea herring is one of the most important food fish in the world. In Europe whole societies were affected by its shifts in abundance. Loss of control over herring fisheries was instrumental in the breakup of the Hanseatic League. In 1881 Thomas Henry Huxley said: "Man, in fact, is but one of a vast co-operative society of herring catchers." The yearly catch is enormous. One school of herring may run not into millions but billions of individual fish; though Huxley may have exaggerated the capacity of the herring population to keep its level in the face of human demands.

To mention another important relative of the alewife, the common or American shad is also a food fish, being something of a delicacy, prized highly for its flesh and roe. It is a larger fish, weighing between six and nine pounds; but it is not so abundant as the alewife.

The menhaden fishery is the largest in the country in terms of weight. Some 800,000,000 pounds of this fish are harvested annually from the Atlantic and Gulf coasts; its present fate is to be turned into fish meal, scrap, and oil. In addition many tons of ground-up menhaden, or "pogies," are used by saltwater anglers to attract bluefish, tuna, or mackerel.

All these herring species are similar in appearance, with silvery scales, easily rubbed off, thin, deep bodies, and tails quite deeply forked.

The alewife belongs to a group of great age in the earth's history, and one which has survived, for one thing, by reason of its numbers, and not by any skill in speed or individual pugnacity. It depends on the crowd rhythm for perpetuation. Its salt-water whereabouts are comparatively unknown, although it is thought it may not go very far afield; but in a run of alewives you might sense not numbers only, but something of the sea's capacious demands that made these fish to measure. Green, gray, silver, they wear its colors, and seem built to nose into its space, or be carried with its moods.

Are there no individuals among them? It is perhaps no term to apply with so manifestly united a company. In any case we are deceived if we try to translate ourselves, our ability to choose, our eyes for pattern and variation, into an animal that can see us at best as an occasional, strange, blurred image appearing above the bank, and to whom everything but the water world is unknown. In a sense we know too little, and so do they, to discuss the matter.

Yet anyone, with a slipping, plunging alewife in his hands, knows it in some degree for its uniqueness. This green-backed, silver-sided water animal, smooth, supple, and muscular, with a sail-like fin on its back is definite enough. Its body is convex-sided, coming to a thin edge at the belly, shaped like shellfish, seeds, or Indian artifacts. From its undershot jaw to its tail, it is clearly a tough fish, and in our experience an adaptable one that knows its way.

This is the "sawbelly" all right. You can very easily feel the serrations, or little teeth, with your fingers—it is one good way of telling alewives from sea herring in the dark. But the name "big-eyed" is perhaps most dramatically true of the alewife. Its black, round, shining eyes are very prominent in proportion to its small head and small mouth. They are large black disks like certain water-worn rocks, or they are great bubbles coming up from a dark depth. I fancied, seeing a tiny image of myself in the alewife's eye, that I was reflected in a deep, impenetrable well.

It is known that a fish's eye is somewhat like ours in that it has a lens, an iris, a cornea, retina, and optic nerve; but that it is designed to see under water, which ours is not. In J. H. Norman's *History of Fishes*, he writes: "The eye, as is well known, acts after the manner of a photographic camera, the two essential parts being the screen or retina at the back, and the lens at the front, which projects an image of the outside world on the screen. The lens of a land vertebrate is somewhat flat and convex on both sides, but in the fish it is a globular body, the extreme convexity being a necessity under water because the substance of the lens is not very much denser than the fluid medium in which the fish lives. The space between lens and retina is filled with a transparent jelly-like substance, the vitreous humor. The transparent outer wall of the eye, the cornea, is somewhat flatter in fishes, and the space between this and the lens is filled by the watery, aqueous humor. In land vertebrates the iris of the eye is capable of great contraction, and, acting like the diaphragm of a camera, regulates the amount of light allowed to enter the eye. In fishes it generally surrounds a rounded pupil, and has comparatively little power of contraction."

I should add that an alewife's eye is somewhat fixed, and not capable of much movement.

Back of the eyes and mouth are the gill covers that protect the gills underneath, which are weak and blood-filled, dark-red overlapping layers, like petals, four on each side. As the fish's gill covers open and close, water passes over the gills, taking oxygen into the blood stream. The alewife's heart, which pumps blood to the gills, is located directly below them.

This is a plankton eater, although it will eat shrimp, small fish, or young eels, on occasion. It has no teeth, or such a semblance of tiny, weak ones, back in its mouth, that they are of little use. The particles of food that come through its mouth are strained through a device known as gill rakers, which act as sieves or filters, in the form of fine hair-like growths mounted on the gill arches, the bony structures on which the gills are also arranged.

A female alewife can be recognized fairly readily by its size. On the average the males run from ten to eleven inches and the females from eleven to twelve, and the males are of course lighter. The proportion of males to females on the inland run seems to be about fifty-fifty.

Alewives weigh anywhere between eight and ten ounces. Part of the weight of both sexes during their spawning migration is accounted for by the roe; in fact, their ovaries and testes may become so enlarged as to fill up a large part of their bodies. The egg sacs of the female vary in color from pink to yellow or yellow-orange, depending on their stage of development. The milt, sometimes called soft roe, of the male, is white and pink.

To sketch a fish so generally is scarcely to know it, but even if I were able to give a good account of its complex skeleton down to the last bone, or discuss all the actions of its nervous system as known so far, I would not have done enough. Our bodies may have chemicals in common with them, but we will never know the fish.

The alewife I took from the water eluded me. Cold-blooded fish, warm-blooded man, the water's triumph caught by the alien air. It slipped my hand and knowledge. "An aquatic vertebrate?" A mystery, though I recognized a life that shone with vibrant persistence, one of nature's particularized energies, a wild texture as old as the animal world, a food that was the beneficent matter of all struggle and greed.

Were there more connections between us that needed exploration? How much fright, how much nerve-threaded darkness, how much throbbing electric quickness might not be receiving me in the distance of that fixed eye? Perhaps we strangers all meet somewhere in each other's sight.

VI
PUZZLES AND
SPECULATIONS

The Herring Run area, small center of commerce and history, had been my starting point, but I had hardly begun to follow the alewives on their whole migratory route between salt water and the ponds above. First of all I had some background of local hearsay to bring into question. Did the herrin' really go all the way down to South America in the wintertime? Was it true that each fish returned to the stream it was born in? Did they come inland on their spawning journey and then die, like the west coast salmon? I overheard a man say, "Poor fish! All that work just to die!" But that was one interpretation I could dispose of early, having seen them go back to salt water the year before. Did they only come in from the Bay at night or on foggy evenings? To find out would take more watching and waiting than I had done so far.

You might deduce this much to start with: the alewives, only a few at first, started to come inland in the spring when the brackish waters from the Stony Brook outlet were warmer than the Bay into which they flowed, if only by a few degrees. They responded with sensitivity to the temperature. If the earliest fish were the oldest, it was possible that the later runs also corresponded to age groups, guessing by their size, and that the youngest came last of all. Evidently schools of alewives stay together during their ocean life according to the years when they were spawned. Yet why, between March and June, any given schools would come in when they did would be hard to tell.

There are places where you can watch the alewives approach, at the junction between tidal and inland waters. At Damariscotta, Maine, they swim up a wide tidal river until a fresh-water stream flows into it from a height above. I was told that the fish are seen massing and circling, sometimes for days, at this point, until by some communicated decision, or joint response—perhaps to pressure of numbers, combined with the right temperature conditions—they start going up. A cold snap may make them drop back to tidewater. In the same way, cold weather may discourage their coming in from Cape Cod Bay.

You can also see them schooling in the Cape Cod Canal at the entrance to the Bournedale run, but not at Stony Brook where the outlet flows into the Bay through low sand dunes, or sand flats at low tide. Whatever the local topography may be, the alewives are evidently attracted to the warmer currents and the lack of salinity in a stream where it flows into salt water.

In general the cause of their moving in together from the offshore depths is their sexual development. I have heard the speculation that this is affected by the increase in light at this stage of the season, but unfortunately know no more about it. In any case at the age of four, or sometimes three, they are ready to spawn, to follow out the new force that is in them, on an old track. Their timing, when to migrate, is a question of generation, a decision that has to be made once again in the earth's timeless schedule. Perhaps there is a comparison to be made once more with the weather, in which the element of surprise is constant during the usual course of the season, the intangible variant still plaguing prediction. The turns to storm or sunshine have their own order in the years beyond the immediate one. Who knows when anything will happen? Suddenly the cicadas start to sing in the August trees. Why that day or hour? Because "conditions are just right"? Perhaps, if we could ever track down all the conditions. Natural acts may be repetitive, but no flight, or song, or new growth has ever existed before at exactly the same time, pitch, or ratio. They are part of the indefinite context of generation.

What about the alewives during their years in the sea? Very little seems to be known. According to *Fishes of the Gulf of Maine* by Bigelow and Schroeder: "The alewife is as gregarious as the herring, fish of a size congregating in schools of hundreds of individuals (we find record of 40,000 fish caught in one seine haul in Boston Harbor) and ap-

parently a given school holds together during most
of its sojourn in salt water. But they are sometimes
caught mixed with menhaden, or with herring. Alewives, immature and adult, are often picked up in
abundance in weirs here and there along the coast,
and it is likely that the majority remains in the
general vicinity of the freshwater influences of the
stream-mouths and estuaries from which they have
emerged, to judge from the success of attempts to
strengthen or restore the runs of various streams.
. . . But it is certain that some of them wander far
afield, for catches up to 3,000 to 4,000 pounds per
haul were made by otter trawlers some 80 miles offshore, off Emerald Bank, Nova Scotia at 60 to 80
fathoms, in March 1936."

They also say, with circumspection: "It seems
likely from the various evidence that the alewives
tend to keep near the surface for the first year or so
in salt water, and while they are inshore when
older. But practically nothing is known of the
depths to which they may descend if (or when)
they move offshore, there being no assurance that
those taken by trawlers were not picked up, while
the trawls were being lowered or hauled up again."

The view that most of the alewives stay in coastal
waters near the fresh waters where they were
hatched seems to be generally accepted, though the
proof is sometimes hard to find. They occur at various depths in the sea as well as considerable distances offshore. They are as likely to be found in
deep as in shallow waters. I am told there are
recorded views that landlocked alewives winter in
the deep waters of Lake Ontario, and that shad, a
close relative, have been found with near-bottom
animals in their stomachs. I also have the information that during the summer of 1956 draggers in

Passamaquoddy Bay were catching a large quantity of alewives and that "it looked as if they were near bottom." Despite some having been picked up in weirs close to the shore at various times during the year, they have not commonly, if at all, been taken by draggers on the continental shelf except when approaching the shore during the spawning season. In other words their oceanic whereabouts have not been pinned down. All we can say, still presuming stocks are local along the coast, is that mature alewives move in from deeper waters offshore in the springtime, progressively later from south to north.

What might seem to be a curious exception to the rule is a run in St. John Harbor, New Brunswick, that occurs in the dead of winter. Alewives are taken there in late January and early February; but I find that this may not be so peculiar a phenomenon as it sounds. To begin with, St. John Harbor is joined with the Bay of Fundy, and when the fish move into it they are still at sea. The reasons for their move at that time is not clear, but as there appears to be winter seining of alewives farther down the coast along the shores of neighboring Charlotte County, it is at least not unbelievable. The alewives then start through the harbor and move up the St. John River to their spawning grounds in the usual migratory months of April and May. I am told by the St. Andrews Biological Station that: "The inflow of the St. John River, particularly in April and May, dilutes the harbor water, especially at the surface. Whether it attracts alewives to the harbor or carries them there by deep circulation is a question." This last point brings up the problem, quite beyond my powers to understand, of how the alewives orient themselves, how they find or are attracted to the waters in which they spawn. We may know very little about their life at sea, but their ability to find a particular stream or river may be an even greater mystery, which is not lessened by the probability that they have been there before. Whether as first-year spawners or repeaters the alewives seem to come back to the streams from which they migrated during the first summer and fall of their lives—when they were not more than a few inches in length. Not consistently—a certain amount of shifting between schools and change of locale may go on. Many go astray like migrating birds, or men out of crowds perhaps, but in general they do tend to return to their home streams. As a proof of this, ponds that were empty of alewives have been stocked with them, and the spawn returned as adults in three or four years' time. This is the "parent stream" theory. With salmon it has apparently been shown to be a fact; although it is not so much the stream they were born in to which they return as the stream in which they grew up. Salmon eggs have been taken out of one river, moved to another, and then the hatched fry were tagged. They migrated to the sea and returned to spawn in the second river where they had their growth.

So what is to account for the alewives being able to find a "parent stream" that might be only a few yards wide, out of all the great stretches of the Atlantic coastline? They left it when they were no more than one and two-fifths to four inches long, but somehow, growing up in the sea, they must always have been oriented to that home base. They may have stayed reasonably near by, but even so this ability is hard to fathom.

Disregarding the question of how they arrived at that point, how could they tell one stream from another? They enter innumerable rivers, streams, inlets, some of them in close proximity. One theory has it that they are able to find their home waters by their characteristic odor, their special composition, to which they were conditioned when young. Even so, how did they get there? How can fish way offshore in waters of a consistent temperature, without any landmarks, tell which direction will take them to their home street? It is quite likely that they would be able to detect the outlet waters where they merged with the sea, but a stream may not reach very far, perhaps a few hundred yards or more at low tide, before being totally absorbed. All the way along the coasts, rivers and streams pour in fresh water, mixed in the estuaries so that it is brackish when it reaches the sea. The sea water increases in salinity as it gets deeper over the continental shelf. An alewife may detect very slight differences in salinity comparatively far out, but we are still not much closer to realizing how it finds its way.

What it amounts to is that no particular factors seem to be able to explain this directional ability of theirs. Not the response to changing currents in the spring sea, not the perception by fish of varying pressures in salt water, or of differences in salinity, nor their possible ability to use the sun as a reference point in navigation . . . none of these approaches have yet solved the great mystery. Do they have some special sense, some perceptiveness, about which we know nothing? Scientists have measured and probed their reactions for a long time, but so far have not found any evidence of a special sensory ability. Biologically, fish do have several unique characteristics. For example, they have an "air bladder" by means of which they are able to adjust themselves to changing densities in the water. They also possess a "lateral line" organ, consisting of a tube or canal under the skin filled with mucus and connected to the nervous system. This sense, closely associated with hearing, enables them to detect vibrations of a very low intensity in the water and to avoid obstacles, such as an approaching bank or another fish. Aside from that, fish can smell, they have sight, and they have a sense of touch and taste.

These known senses are what scientists count on in investigating the migratory behavior of fish. They test their responses to different stimuli. On that basis, one of the most recent directions to be explored centers around the environmental factors which the fish are subjected to, such as currents, temperatures, the physical and chemical nature of the waters through which they swim. These factors are supposed to guide them successively on their migrations and to be so consistent year after year that the responsive fish return to their streams of origin because they never got off the track. Different schools, or age groups, of alewives would go to separate streams, because they responded differently, as Gerald B. Collins puts it in his study of alewives at Bournedale, "to the existing patterns of environmental stimuli." Homing, from the environmentalists' point of view, is neither a matter of memory nor mystery.

I do not have enough knowledge behind me to discuss such a method or approach, but it does seem to have the advantage of comprehensiveness, of taking the whole journey in. It does not depend on any single factor to explain migratory behavior,

and it provides a good long track of exploration, step by step.

Whether the migrant fish behave as mechanically as this suggests, or whether the factors involved are separately either as consistent as they are supposed to be, or amount in the aggregate to as much as they should, remains to be seen. We are still in the realm of theory, however rationally expressed, and do not know yet how the fish find their destination.

Can a fish judge its course by the sun, or by the circulation of the waters of which it is so much a part? Can we talk about a homing instinct, or orienting ability, in connection with it? What are we defining? I don't think I beg the question by finding it pertinent that civilized human beings have to some extent lost their ability to find their way in the woods, or no longer rise and sleep with the sun, or that they are not aware of the changing tides. Some old directional knowledge may still be innate in us, though we seem to think we have no need of it. Our puzzle, or lack of definition, may lie with ourselves as much as the alewives. In any case, what we try to find out by fact or abstraction is already known to the fish.

They are still ahead of us. So much of their motion seems to be a part of the race as a whole, synonymous with its great water world, that it is almost as if they found their way like the wind and tides, elemental forces that we find it hard to evaluate. We try to pin down that which expands immeasurably beyond us.

VII
PORT OF ENTRY

With a certain amount of half-determined knowledge behind me, I decided early one morning to follow up the question of how far the brackish waters of the Stony Brook outlet extended into Cape Cod Bay, and so went down to Paine's Creek. This is the place where the stream, which has been winding through tidal marshes like a small river, ends in a basin where several dories are moored, then takes a last turn and long curve, cutting through low dunes anchored by beach grass that border the sands. I saw a kingfisher rising up over the creek, a green crab shifting along the shelving bank; and on the beach were the remains of a black duck, sodden, bedraggled, the feathers loaded with wet sand, the breastbone sticking up like the white prow of a helmet, flies buzzing over it—the smell of salted carrion around it.

The sound of the waters along the creek is constant and musical, following and followed up, broadly roaring, rushing, or slipping lightly, as they rise, pushed back by the incoming tide, or run out low and easy with the ebb. At low tide these creek waters spread their channels and fingered rivulets some three hundred yards straight out over the sands, to a point where they are joined by the waters of Quivett Creek which has an inlet a few hundred yards upshore to the west. Then the one channel finds its way past a fish weir until it is lost in the salt waters coming in over a long bar in the distance. The alewives also swim into the other creek; though not in the numbers that run up Stony Brook, because of less access to spawning grounds beyond.

The tide was well out when I started to follow, or rather taste the fresh water over the sands. The Brewster flats, as they are called, were alive with light and constantly changing where they stretched out on the earth's curve. Minor investigation took place in maximum horizons. I walked toward the weir, or fish trap, one of three in the distance, long-poled stockades a quarter of a mile or so apart, hung with nets like veils or the peaked coifs of nuns. A silver sun was beginning to lift through sheets of low fog, and a cool wind blew across the sands. It made my ears boom with that hollow sound of deep marine that you hear in a shell. I saw a small flock of brant standing off, their heads alert for danger, ready to thrust up and go when

I came. I approached lines of brown dunlins, red-backed sandpipers, sanderlings, black-bellied plovers, which stood and scurried, peeped and cried, flew forward into the wind for short stretches, and came down again.

As the sun rose farther up, clouds began to be reflected in the lanes between the ribbed sands, and there were thousands of gulls standing in a silver, immeasurable distance, while those sharp, light arrows, the terns, flew overhead. The flats with their brown deserts, their lakes, and pools, and veins, were like the patterned floors, the reaches of the great civilizations of man. The dawn fogs blew off. I was waking up to an architecture of space.

Now from these tidal areas the plains of the sea rove out indefinitely. You can get a look at the universal map without benefit of signposts, and the coming on of fish represents great standards of inevitability.

"But look," a scientist might say, "in this unlimited space of yours, the mating animal only has a tiny area to travel in; a few miles at sea, if in the case of the alewives, they do stay offshore, and perhaps two or three miles inland. They are limited in space, and limited in numbers accordingly."

True, but we might add that it is this limitation, in alewives at least, that makes increase possible. They are one of the most easily managed of all marine species. Clear out the obstructions in their way; restock a lake and river system, or pond and stream, and the fish return, the population rises. Alewife management depends on their almost relentless drive to go back where they came from. No life insists on its locality more strongly. Home in their case is a definite route, a round way, small if

you like, but spinning in larger circles, where birth
leads back to its necessity.

So I walked the sea lands, following the alewives' avenue of approach. Well beyond the weir
I began to get in too deep to qualify as an investigator. I judged that the brackish water of the outlet
went at least five hundred yards out, and probably
several hundred yards more than that, before it
flowed into the salt waters of the Bay and then
was lost in them. It seemed, during low tide at
least, that the alewives might detect the fresh water
reasonably far out in the Bay, disregarding the
question of how they arrived at that point.

As I went back across the wind again, under the
hovering, crying birds, and saw where the waters of
the two creeks came out, the strange fish knowledge of where to go was still unbelievable. I
imagined alewives coming in here, or to a shore
where there were even more creek inlets fairly close
together, and wondered whether the schools joined
in the Bay like concentric circles and then sepa-
rated, each going to the stream in which it grew
up. I also wondered about that supposed chemical
sense, or sense of odor, that might explain the alewife's knowledge of its home stream. Would not
the composition of the waters of any one stream
change greatly at various times of the year? It must
be very different in the hot summer, when the little
alewives come down to salt water, from the cool
months of spring when the adults came in. Would
that not be just as important a factor as the
stream's difference from another close by?

Two miles farther up along the shore is another
inlet at the mouth of Sesuit Creek. Many years ago
the Sesuit and Quivett inlets were interconnected

at some point back in their tidal marshes; and before the roads and banks were built that now divide them there was also more access to several ponds in the vicinity, both large and small. Since the glacial ponds of Cape Cod seem to fill up and dry out in time, turning to wooded or grassy hollows, it is possible too that the alewives had even more entryways, and went even farther inland, having longer fresh-water routes to travel—water veins open and flowing everywhere. In any event, the alewife population now starting up these two inlets is very small compared to that of Stony Brook, which shows that the fish are balanced in numbers according to the relative ease or difficulty of getting inland to adequate spawning grounds. In part, it also seems to be an added proof of the parent stream theory. The fish know their way. For whatever reason, and whether or not they are entirely consistent in coming back to the exact stream, it seems to us that they have a remarkable sense of direction, although, for all we know, it may not be any more remarkable than the accuracy of the tides or the timing of the sun.

VIII
THE
COMMON NIGHT

Did the alewives choose the night or late evening hours to come in by? So I had been told. By daylight evidence, the fish population increased at the Herring Run on the mornings following a nightly high tide. I had also heard that there were more alewives running during the tides of the full moon, in the farthest monthly reaches of ebb and flood; but this was a correlation that would be hard for me to make without more years to judge by. In the middle of May on the days just after the first quarter of the moon, which came on the sixteenth, the fish seemed to be running just about as hard as they did during the days preceding the full moon in April, which had appeared on the twenty-fourth. Judging accordingly, it seemed as though their migration had its own ebb and flood during those months. All this was not much better than impression plus hearsay, but there seemed to be some justice to the night tide theory, so, to begin with, I went down to the shore late one evening during an incoming tide to see if there might be any sign of the alewives.

About eight o'clock, an hour before high tide, the tide was running strongly in at Paine's Creek. The channel in the marshes flooded over its banks and marsh grasses were floating and stirring as the swaying waters rose around them. It was near dark. I could see some seaweed flinging by against the sandy bottom at the mouth of the creek, and a big, ghostly green eel slithered up at the edge of the bank the waves were licking, seemed to look up at me, looped back into the water, and disappeared; but it was too dark to see much more than those black clumps of seaweed racing by. I saw a group of gulls standing in shoal waters beyond the beach, where waves were rolling in hard under a steady northwest wind. The sun's cauldron had dropped down, a raw, glistening orange-red, into the sea and back of the curved horizon, leaving its horizontal flush behind.

I walked back under the lee of the sand banks bordering the curving creek. The tide was pulsing and roaring, its waters loping in to the creek which began to turn a harder, darker blue under the sky. Then I began to hear the innumerable soft slaps of fish breaking the surface. The alewives were making their entry from the sea.

And the gulls proclaimed their coming. Out in

the Bay, they began to gather by the hundreds, clambering up with a scrambled yelping and hollering. The last smoky, red line of sunset was disappearing and they hovered over it in a maddened, high, wide swarm like huge bees. It grew darker, and a black-crowned night heron, or "quawk," sometimes "quok," a name true to the sound it makes, flew by with rounded wings against a star. The gulls began to disappear, streaming faintly like ashes against the last fires on the sea, but still crying vastly and collectively toward a world of distances. And in terrible simplicity, the alewives were swimming toward the inland gauntlet they would have to run, having a title, by their common, wild, and ancient advent, to all great kindled things. Who will see more than that in his short life, with its many meetings and separations?

I by an old and natural right felt a fierce water-deep wonder of the spirit. The beyondness in me went back to its beginnings. I thought of the nights on which children I have known were born, and of the voyages of war, leave-takings at railroad stations and at ports of embarkation, and of dreams in which I struggled toward new meetings and other lives. The wind blew through the arches of the stars, and the surfaces of the dipping earth, water, and sky in their lasting communion made me dizzy. I felt a cold inevitable grandeur, below consciousness, a swim and go in an uttermost wild world, past home or my life's memory.

So by this evidence the alewives came in at night, and, as a further discovery not to be denied, so had I. Perhaps it was the closest I would ever get to the nonhuman fish in a darkness where all the components of existence ran the same race. That real depth, fish-oriented, nakedly omnipotent, fills men when they recognize it with more awe than their limited worlds can encompass.

As I started back, about a quarter of an hour before the full tide, headlights swept over where the road ended at the shore, and in a minute or two a couple of fishermen lurched down the sand with high rubber waders on, carrying their casting rods. They stood on the beach in the dark, one of them coaching the other in baiting his hook. I came up and spoke to them, hardly able to make out their faces. The older one, he who did the coaching, told me that they had just got a pail of herrin' from the Brewster run to use as bait. They had hopes that there would be some bass here, the famous "stripers" chasing the alewives in. They brought their long rods sideways and back to sling the bait out into the black and silver waves. The older man spoke low words against the wind, and I strained to hear him. Suddenly he thought he felt what must be alewives nosing his line and bumping against it on their way by into the mouth of the inlet. Last year, he told me, he had seen hundreds of them dead on the flats, and the gulls, he said, had slit their sides open as if with knives to get the roe. The waves had begun to slacken off when I left, and the fishermen were still casting, but without much hope of a strike.

IX
THE HUNT

For a little while I felt satisfied that I knew the alewives only chose to come in on the night or late evening tides, until they proved me wrong. I say *they* proved me wrong because I give myself no credit for more than moderately ignorant perseverance in following up a hypothesis. The alewives did a good deal of proving and disproving for me. They would probably show me up again.

At the beginning of the third week in May there had been a fresh run of fish crowding into the Herring Run, if not as heavily as those that came in a month before. After the migration starts there are

very few days in either April or May when some
fish are not to be seen in the brook waters. One
man can only judge by eye plus the amount of
barrels being hauled out as to how many there are
in any period, but there may have been a climacti-
cal run during the week after the nineteenth of
May when the high tides came at night. On the
twenty-first I had been taking temperature read-
ings, out of curiosity and to keep up with the advancing season. It had been around 40 degrees
Fahrenheit during the night and rose to 47 at 7:30
A.M., 53 at 9:00 and 55 at 9:30 as the sun's rays
heated the land. Just offshore, down the beach from
Paine's Creek, at around 9:30, high tide being at
9:57, the temperature of the salt water, more consistent than the land, was 49, and the reading I
then took of the brackish water at the mouth of the
creek was 51.

I noticed a small crew of alewives in the tea-
dark channel. Had they come in the night before?
They were schooling back and forth, as though
getting accustomed to the waters in which they
newly found themselves.

The tide began to turn. The waters going out at
the creek mouth were yellow-green. I walked along
the beach, and the surface of the Bay was long and
smooth, a blue-green stretching and easing under
a light wind with purple patches showing above
seaweed and shelving banks of peat. I could hear
the slow, gentle, labial sounds of the lightly ebb-
ing waters. There was a small school of unidentifi-
able minnows turning and slipping-in-silver just offshore. A long frieze pattern of gull tracks showed,
where the sand was damp, crisscrossed here and
there by the little tracks of sandpipers and plovers.

This cool, seaside world seemed full of equipoise to me, with a searching air of freedom playing over.

There had been several clumps of herring gulls standing in shoals in the creek where it flowed out into the Bay. I noticed that some of them had begun to fly up. Then I saw a great black-backed gull swoop at the water farther out, and a number of herring gulls beyond it plummeting down, then chasing each other over the surface. They were after fish, but what kind? I went off for twenty minutes to get some field glasses, and by the time I returned the gulls had increased by the hundreds. Big clouds of them were circling and moving in from up the coast, higher and higher like drifting paper, some of them way up in the blinding blue sky, but coming closer, joining the feast.

I could see that the gulls were diving straight down the course of the Paine's Creek waters where they went out into the Bay, and that the fish they flung up between them clearly had the general size and shape of alewives. What was going on then was a great interception. The fish in their deliberate way had found the mouth of the creek, and made their instinctive move to go in, but as the water became shallower during the ebb tide they were ripe prey for the birds and there was no turning back.

The violent, reckless activity of the gulls went on all morning. In the way they have of riding each other: "You've got it. Show you can keep it!" they were picking up fish, dropping them, and running away with them again, in a scrambling frenzy. There seemed to be almost more excitement, more energy, spent in the chase than in the fruits of it, though they gobbled what they could. I could hear

an over-all sound of struggle as their wings rushed
and they yawked and screamed. This world seemed
pantingly, gruntingly, wildly busy.

The victims of this natural slaughter seemed to
have moved on a little, with their fatal determina-
tion, but as the tide and morning ebbed the white,
frantic crowd above them seemed to stay in the
same general area. It was not likely that many fish
managed to reach the inlet. I imagined them dashing from side to side or circling in panic, the crowd
knowing nothing but its own entity and safety. I
talked to a man who was watching the scene from
the window of his car. He told me that there had
been a high bluff, washed away some years back,
from which you could actually see the fish in the
water as they struggled to swim in.

"We had a good stream went out there that
wouldn't a happened," he said, suggesting that if
there were a deeper channel meeting the Bay waters, most of the fish might be able to get up the
creek in comparative safety.

Along this stretch of rhythmic work of greed and
death little groups of gulls began to settle down on
the water, glutted and loaded down. The long
lines of them, looking like white shoals, rested on
the water upshore, digesting their meal. Low tide
that afternoon came at 3:57. By two o'clock when
the sands began to show, well out toward the weirs,
the great tribal company of gulls were finished with
the hunt. For a mile along the flats they were standing into a stiff wind. In the distance I could see a
litter of dead fish along the bed of the creek waters.
When I walked out I saw them, silver, blue, and
white, with brassy tints from the sun, flung along,
strewn on like debris through a wide city square.

Even though there may be no waste in nature—

with everything used, fired, and consumed in the interactions of the living world—what an enormous, careless expenditure! The bed of the outgoing waters was paved with this alewife coinage for hundreds of yards. Each one I picked up, and there were thousands, had its body scraped and clawed, or its head torn, its eyes gouged out. For everyone gobbled during the chase there must have been many more left uneaten. Remembering what the night fishermen had said, it seemed like an indiscriminate feast, and it was not clear to me that the gulls were primarily after roe. But since fish eggs are a delicacy to other animals, gulls may find a special enjoyment in them too.

So the alewives did not choose to come in by night or evening only, seeing that they chose to come in by day—provided there was much choice in the matter. I heard the theory put forward that they must have been chased in by bass; but if they were so chased, it did not seem likely that they would choose the narrow waters of this particular creek for refuge, or have that much calculation in them. That is not why they came in. Those thousands of years the alewives had migrated provided their own track. The fish knew instinctively when and where to go, and all risks were incidental to that. The only possibility was that they might have been schooling around in the farthest reaches of the creek waters in the bay and were hurried in by the bass; but they were there first. Many others may have gone in the night before. Those trying to come in during the morning waited their turn after an ebb tide. This rhythmic deliberation and then going seemed very characteristic of the fish as I had watched them in inland waters, and in a larger way it might be similar to their schooling in salt water. I found out subsequently that the alewives coming into the Bournedale run in the Cape Cod Canal do so both day and night, but there is less chance of the gulls intercepting them there because of the deeper waters.

I went down to Paine's Creek the following morning, May 22, and the frenzied hunt was going on again. I had checked the previous night and did so the night of this day too and there were no fish coming in, so far as I could tell. There was no sign of them in the water during the late evening, no sound of their soft slapping on the surface later on.

It is my impression that though they start into the creek in the dark—perhaps not later than ten-thirty or eleven o'clock—they do not move upstream very much until daylight comes. Sunlight stimulates them, or, to be exact, its radiation. You can see them swimming up faster in Stony Brook after the bright sunlight warms the water in the morning.

They might enter the creek more successfully under the protection of fog, or darkness, combined with deep water, but did not prefer such conditions to broad daylight. When the temperature was right and they were physiologically ready, alewife schools began to move in from salt water on an incoming tide . . . swing in might be a better term, since a circular movement is characteristic and sends them on. According to my observation, incidentally, this is very likely to be counterclockwise. In any case the power and direction of the migration came from their combined rhythmic impulses.

Alewives seemed to me to demand a study of universal motions and their interrelationships. The body of a fish must have in it the declination of the globe and all its years. If I had read some of my limited science reading correctly, there was a time system in the world of life which had nothing to do with clocks, and their specific minutes and hours. It was built into its creatures so that their stages of development, their growth and movements, followed the direction and change of all other forces affecting them. It is a running world; and who, in that context, is more automatic than another?

X
TRANSITION:
SALT AND FRESH

The change, for those fish that make it in, is from salt to fresh, wide to narrow, deep to shallow. Watched at Paine's Creek in the first sheltered inland curve, the movement of those I was able to see was like the movement of tides and estuary waters, a flowing back and forth, a waving and interweaving. Some dropped back like leaves, then swam up again with the rest as they all turned together. At the start of an incoming tide—when the salt water moved in under the fresh and the creek began to rise—the fish seemed stimulated and swam faster, back and forth against it. Then gradually, though it was hard to see them in the high tide waters, they appeared to move farther up the inlet.

It was an encounter at the dramatic approaches of sea and land, on the long shoreline where continuous transitions are made between water and earth and air.

If you say the "anadromous habit" started somewhere in geologic time, it is difficult to conceive of, and it is probably not accurate, in the sense that these adaptations to environment do not start so much as develop and evolve. In any event the incredibly long history of the earth is not broken down with any facility. First of all, leaving out the question of whether fish originally evolved in fresh waters or the sea, and then blithely skipping one hundred million years or so, you have an evolved race of alewives, established residents of the sea. As to their habit of spawning in fresh water, it is possible that alewives, like other coastal fish, may gradually have explored the inland rivers and streams, until they began to use their comparative quiet and refuge in which to spawn. Along the northern coasts their inland migration would have been interrupted during the glacial epochs, and their range would have started farther to the south. There are landlocked varieties of alewife in Lake Ontario and in New York State, which also suggests a period when continental glaciers retreated, leaving an access by water to inland lakes from the sea which was later cut off. In any case this anadromous habit was arrived at gradually, involuntarily, over a very long time. But, in a sense, what you see *now*, your center of history, is a routine which is neither old nor new but both various and inexorable, having in it the pull of the land, the blood of the sea.

This starting, circulatory movement of the few
small schools I had seen was succeeded by the
swimming of steady herds in the brown water of
the channel. I couldn't find them at first. On the
ebb tide, when the water had receded enough from
the banks along the inlet I walked there for a while
and then cut across the tidal marsh. The day was
cool and fresh, with a light northeast wind lifting
in, and it smelled of the sea. (You can live a mile
or so inland on the narrow peninsula of Cape
Cod, in the towns or oak woods, and never smell
that rich combination of salt water, shellfish, and
tidal marsh, unless the wind is from the right
quarter, with a special condition of the atmos-
phere.) Light rippled up the broad inlet—the coppery waters seemed to move slowly and reliantly.
The season had hatched its enthusiasms everywhere, from flies, to crabs, to birds. The tidal
ground was pitted with holes made by fiddler
crabs. They backed away in front of me, the males
comically holding up their one big claw—little
characters of a dull metal-blue, with bubbling
mouths—and disappeared into the safety of their
burrows. Ahead of me nine Canada geese, which
had been resting and feeding in the marshes, un-
folded their wings and lunged up and out toward
the Bay.

Then two black ducks flew off quacking in their
deep, wild way. I saw where a deer had left fresh
hoofprints in the mud; looking down at them made
me notice many tiny shells, newly hatched whelks
perhaps, carried in by the tide, strewn between the
stiff spikes of the marsh grass; and I found a couple of empty pint bottles, sometimes as common in
these parts as Kleenex beside the highways of
America. Insects, shells, ducks, geese, crabs, wind,

cloud rack overhead, brilliance and shadows on the tidal ground—many lifetimes of learning. Is there any man who knows the length and breadth of anything, let alone a creek? Yet such a place keeps announcing its novelties and exacting from us whatever love and discipline we are capable of; or so I felt, challenged in the keen air and the high glitter of the light.

Several hundred yards around another bend in the inlet, where it was some twelve to fifteen feet wide, I looked down into the water and saw them again. The dark channel was alive with them. It had a floor of turning, slowly moving alewives. A few at the end of this school would run quickly back, revealing their shadows on the bottom. The procession moved back and forth, as smoothly as the flow of the water, and across the entire width of the channel. They were more numerous in the areas where the sun hit the water directly.

Some of them looked torn and scarred. On that basis, and because many thousands had either been trucked off from the Herring Run in barrels by this time, or had reached the ponds, spawned, and returned to the Bay, you could not say categorically that they were all moving inland. As the season develops you can always find spent fish on their way to salt water running through those still heading up to the spawning areas. Aside from watching their movements, one method of distinguishing between the two classes of fish is to see if they bear any white patches on their backs and sides. A certain number of the spent fish will show fungus growths after a period of time in fresh water. What seems to happen is that an alewife, attacked by a gull or predatory fish or flung against sharp rocks, will at first show a "scaling" from the damage.

This scaling, unless it is more than that, a mortal wound, is likely to develop into a fungus growth, which sometimes covers a large part of a fish's body; but without, apparently, any added injury. I believe experiment proves that the fungus disappears fairly soon after the fish affected are back in salt water.

The returning alewives will stay for a while in the brackish water of the inlet, resting and feeding. They are spare and hungry and will feed on shrimp, small eels, and small fish. Alewives that by chance stay longer than the others in fresh water have been known to chase and eat their own young, if they were small enough to swallow.

Their basic salt-water diet is plankton. The copepods and amphipods—tiny animals similar to the well-known sand hoppers, beach fleas, water fleas, or small shrimp—provide the staple part. On their inland migration they will not eat much of anything. They are in the service of a mission, and they fast. Still there may be occasions when they snap at lures. I have heard of some, migrating inland, that were caught by fishermen casting with flies at the Herring River in Harwich, on the south side of the Cape.

Those herds now in the brown waters of the channel seemed to be gradually moving inland as the day advanced, and I guessed that for most of them it was the journey up.

As I watched them there was a slight, quick change of wind, a shift in the breeze that flicked the water, and in the crosshatches this made on the bright surface all the fish disappeared. Then the surface cleared and I could see them again, swimming through a rippling weave of light that was reflected on the channel floor.

They meandered along, an occasional lively one dashing through the rest, or rushing up to the surface. I could hear light plops, faint flips along the water. I walked closer to the edge so that my shadow fell across them, and they turned back in one quick and graceful stampede, some of them dashing to deeper water under the opposite bank. That so many separate entities should have such an immediate response to one another that they all moved like the beat of a wing was hard for one individual to understand.

Alewives are able to stand the quick change from salt to fresh water without any trouble. It would kill some other kinds of fish, but neither the alewife fry growing up in fresh water nor adults growing up in the sea seem to mind being taken out of one medium and plunged into another. They are adapted to both. On the other hand, repeated changes, such as occur sometimes under certain conditions in tidal estuaries, are said to be able to kill them.

These changes, incidentally, are registered in an alewife's scales. To read them is difficult and requires a competent biologist. In general they mark physiological changes, such as occur when young alewives go from fresh to brackish water, or when the adults spend some time in fresh water before returning to the sea. An alewife's age can be determined because a record of each spawning migration is etched on the scales.

I had seen them flashing and swarming inland up in the Herring Run area, but in this wide channel were new motions that needed more patience and information to be understood. For example, where the fish eddied and wheeled under the dazzling rays, I noticed one group idling in front of a

submerged sand bar or reef that ran across the
channel. I waited there for three-quarters of an
hour before the fish showed signs of any common
impulse to cross over it. One or two dashed over
sportively to chase a minnow and then sped back,
but the rest of them—a hundred or more—would
make no move. Finally, after many circling approaches by the whole crowd, the measure of their
circle came closer and closer out of the brown
water to the brightly lit, coppery bar, until some
of the vanguard spilled over. Then more and more
sped and skittered over until the move was ac-
complished. Why? Were they afraid of the brightness? Did the contrast in light stop them in some
way? This would hardly seem consistent with what
I had found out so far. Perhaps it was just routine
to their motion. Evidently alewives idle in the
deeper channels where the velocity of the water is
slower and easier to swim in. They respond to the
relative force of the flow. Where the current is more
uniformly rapid, and they are going up against it,
they progress steadily. And perhaps the bar formed
an eddy behind it, so that the water where they
swam moved against the current in the channel
and they were unable to tell their direction.

The alewife hordes puzzled me as they moved
slowly but definitely through the channel. A new
animal, moving to unknown needs is hard to understand. You grasp for some translation between
you that will not come. Relationships in the water
world seem to need other senses than your own. It
could be said that to understand the transition
of the alewives from salt to fresh water and back
you must know about the effect of the endocrine
glands on the reproductive system, as well as adaptations of the kidney, along with the temperature,

the time of the tides, and the chemical composition of a particular stream—just to begin with. If you are wise and devoted enough to put all the known factors together, you may come out with a unified interpretation, and be abreast of the latest theories of process. Knowledge is the motion by which the human animal may come closest to a fish. Still I looked in my ignorance for another familiarity in which we shared. Where the sea pushed inland and the alewives moved ahead or returned, I saw an indefinite route, of surpassing, complex elaboration; but in their pulse and tempo I felt something that gave me present assurance, and a touch of joy.

XI
UP THE VALLEY

When you leave the channel that elbows through the tidal marshes and then goes under the shore road, Route 6 A, through the valley ending at the Herring Run, you go from one living community to another. You leave the thousands of fiddler crabs tunneling through marshy ground, the fat, olive-colored little salt-water minnows, or mummichogs, darting through green clouds of muck in the warm pools left by the tide, and muskrats, kingfishers, herons, ducks, or gulls. Some are permanent residents, others are itinerants, but all are presently bound together in the tidal grounds. They feed off one another, being both producers and consumers of food, and so sustain the balance of all their lives together. Such communities are the principal study of the ecologists—the interrelationship of living things in their environment.

The alewife migrates from sea to ponds through the inland vein, from crabs and shellfish to robins, and frogs beyond the tide. Its migration runs through several different life communities, of which it is not strictly a part, although its progeny, the fry, will be a part of the food chain all the way along, the prey of many different kinds of fish and birds, and eaters themselves of food the ponds provide. But the alewife's migrant continuity is like the water itself that runs unceasingly down the valley, and ties all the life together that adjoins it.

The stream, on the north side of the shore road, used to run up the center of the valley where there is still a ditch dividing once cultivated cranberry bogs, but the watercourse was long since diverted to the eastern side of the valley. It was in that direction I went one half-showery, half-sunny day for a further exploration, but first by way of the short, bordering range of hills before going down again. Hills and scoured valley were left by the most recent continental glacier as it melted back from the terminal moraine of Cape Cod perhaps some twelve thousand years ago. I climbed the steep slope on the west side of the valley, nearest the Herring Run. Below me the long, snaky turns of the run went down from its rocky top where the waters were churning white and spilling over. As I walked up and down the slopes and across the small ravines between them, I could hear voices receding down by the Herring Run; and then a woodchuck whipped a whistle and dove when I came up, its brown rump disappearing into a freshly dug hole, which had an arc of sandy yellow dirt piled outside. On the way there were wild cherry, viburnum, hawthorn, pitch pine, and juniper sparsely growing, and I passed a dipping stone wall that marked an old boundary line. I picked up a wing from the remains of a dead herring gull on the ground, put it before the light wind, and was struck with what broad strength it held the air. As I came toward that knob of a hill where the gulls congregated, they flocked away with a simultaneous rush of wings and went crying high toward the Bay. The hill was bald, except for a few wild rosebushes on its crown, and its slopes were covered with a wild pink, moss campion, and patches of sorrel made more profuse by nitrogen and ammonia from gull droppings. On the other side of the valley there was a wood of twirling, gnarled, gray tupelo trees with the pink of their buds still showing. Bay waters and the curving, final shore carried distance out along with the gulls; while this valley with its dips and slopes and the migratory waves of life to which its land and water were hosts seemed wide enough for many worlds.

As I clambered down a slope toward the stream, three ducks that were coming in to settle on marshy ground changed course, two black-crowned night herons flew out of a tree, clucking like hens, and a yellowlegs stalking through muddy peninsulas flew up and away, its sickle wings in reckless flight, with a cry both tremulous and sharp. Everything fled before me. I might be a part of these communities myself but as an itinerant, it seemed, and a dangerous one. How difficult it is to prove to anything but domestic animals, long since tamed and lost, that a man is not dangerous! Men have a hard time trying to prove it to themselves.

I had come down near the point where Stony Brook started to turn to the east side of the valley. The banks behind me were streaming with spring water and the wet edges were lush with new growth: lettuce-green grass, succulent-looking leaves of skunk cabbage, fiddlehead ferns newly uncurling, and clumps of violets, flowers of a sky-delicate light blue. At this edge of the valley the water was full of thicketed islands, hummocks, and muddy shallows, but as the stream stretched on, ten to twelve feet wide, the current swung along at a man's fast walk over a brown and sandy bottom, and in it, constantly eddying by and turning over, were innumerable silver fish scales, debris of the striving and death at the Herring Run, several hundred yards behind.

Where the stream turned at right angles across the valley it was bordered by a low man-made dike. Halfway down the dike, at the end of a long narrow ditch bisecting the old bogs, was the remains of a *stop water*, a kind of three-sided dam designed to raise or lower the water in a cranberry bog to its desired level. I looked down into its still, dark square of water and there was a split-second rush of a fish, and perhaps two or three others coiling in the small space together. They may have been spawning. In any case, intentionally or not, they had come down the ditch instead of by the main stream and could go no farther. There are many areas in a run, side pools, ditches, marshy land, to which some alewives may be sidetracked, before the main spawning grounds.

I saw a few later in a dead-end offshoot of the

Herring River that looked very much as if they were trying to go back, though I have no reason to suppose they felt that they had made a mistake. If they were not ready to spawn they may have circled back with the ebb tide, which reached that point, and found the main flow where they had lost it on the way up.

I have idly wondered whether a single fish, isolated from its brethren, might not suffer some kind of unknown hell of estrangement. I have seen one swimming wildly down a narrow ditch off a tidal inlet as if it knew the crowd had left it behind, and was frantic to get back. Still, for all we can say about their lack of consciousness, they carry out their great decisions, their deep harmonies, together, by natural laws which we ourselves cannot completely explain, and by which we too may carry out our migrant purposes.

The creek flowed on through banks tangled with poison ivy, blueberry bushes, briars, and grapevines —at times almost impassable. Once, as I peered out from the tangle, I saw a bird I had never seen outside a field guide—a Virginia rail, moving along a muddy shelf under the opposite bank. It moved almost humped over, neck and head forward, like a great mouse, with a docked tail and red-orange beak. Then farther on I saw an egret with head and slender neck above some high pitch pines, pure sky-white, Grecian, out of a stately, impenetrable world, almost too secret for an ecologist.

Where the stream was wider and the shallow water flowed along, lightly and unobstructed, a group of some ten or twelve fish ran easily across it. Then they stopped and circled with the current like a nest of eels, in a slow, fluid mass.

I turned back. After light sunshine there was a

faint shower, a spray of rain. The valley was full of
sound. A slow plane flew over; a truck's gears
ground over the road: I heard a song sparrow stak-
ing out his territory; crows cawed; blue jays gave
harsh and silvery shouts; I heard my own breath
and the almost silent touch of cool air and rain
spray on the ground—a narrow valley, but with
melodious resources from everywhere. Why "back
to nature"? I thought. Is there anything in it but
forwardness?

In the stretch below the Herring Run again I
suddenly saw, in the blank, dark water under gray
skies, a wave, an eruption, a rushing ahead of a
group of fish. Then they moved over to the side of
the shallow stream, thirty or forty of them, and
stayed there almost stationary for a while in deeper,
slower currents where an overhanging shrub shaded
the water. I threw a stick in their direction . . .
when it hit the water they wheeled wildly on their
group axis, but stayed in the same place. Then in a
minute or two they all made a break for open water
at once, and I noticed that another group had come
in unseen behind them. They would progress in this
way, group after group, until they met the denser
population below the fish ladders. One of them
would come out first with a kind of flitting, darting, weaving forward against the current and the
rest wheeled in behind it.

I took off my shoes and waded out into the
stream. A lead fish working its way back and forth
with the current swung around as I came and fled
back. I stood still for a while, noticing that the
gulls I chased out of the valley had returned and
were hovering over, chuckling, crying, mumbling,
or barking like seals. After a few minutes of waiting the fish came right through and around my

legs. My slightest change in posture would send the ones in front looping back, but they still kept coming. It was a quickening thing to see a fish race up in a long reach and then drop part way back again—a tentative, fast exploration of the current, the living current as perpetual as its own communicated impulses.

One hundred yards or so upstream the alewives covered the stream bed where Stony Brook's divided waters met. Some schooled slowly around below the unsurmountable falls, the rocks of death, the majority headed up the main stream toward the fishway where hundreds were massed, slipping and turning, arched in the white waters. Fishways are so designed as to allow the alewives an easier way to mount an incline, but they do have the effect of concentrating them in narrow quarters. The resting pools are compartments deep enough to check the velocity of the water and so permit the fish to wait before leaping on again. Even so the water roared down with great force on the alewives crammed in them. I could hardly hold my cupped hand against it. As they leaped up they were tunneled in spouts of water, and then they would flip through the boiling surface from one pool to the next, sometimes being thrown back to try again.

XII
THE
IMPERFECT LADDER

There is no such thing, I have been told by men who were in the business of making them, as a good or even adequate fishway. There is always an imbalance between the purposes they serve and the results. All the same, fishways are the best we can do to remedy a situation that blocked great populations of fish from entry to their natural routes. They are built to try and bring back what man has taken away; though it should be said that they are as much in man's interest as the alewife's. Commerce is the main benefactor of their success.

Fishways help open up free passage to the fish,

and so increase their numbers. In a good fishway alewives can be counted or sampled. They can be taken out and transferred to other areas that are to be stocked with them. In other words, the removal of obstacles and the construction of a fish ladder means, in most cases, that a run can either be introduced or improved, and, above all, kept under control.

The trouble is that they cannot be built so as to result in free-and-easy passage for the fish at all times. In fact, if they are not properly placed, they can even be a hindrance. A fishway requires engineering and research in its preparation. They vary greatly, of course, according to local conditions. A fish ladder's length depends on the distance of the slope down which a flow is directed, or the kind of banks, rocks, or stream formation through which it is built. I imagine there are no ideal specifications. For alewives, fishway construction depends in general on the size and habits of the fish and the nature of the waters in which they travel. The great fish ladders built for salmon at the Bonneville Dam, on the Columbia River, have pools in them that are forty feet wide, sixteen feet long, and six feet deep, each being a foot above the other. One foot is no problem to the salmon, which have been known to leap as high as ten.

At Stony Brook the pools on the down, or north, side of the road are ten in number and various in size, extending some distance downstream. The first six are smaller and deeper than the others, being so designed as to round a bend in the stream. Their depth, subtracting several inches of sand that keeps washing down from the road, is about two feet.

On the upper side, above the seining pool, leading from one of the pond outlets, is a straight ladder, some twenty feet long. Its pools are four and a half feet square and twenty-eight inches deep, each being about five inches above the other, thus graduating to fit the slope.

Whatever their design, fishways are all built so as to assure the alewives quick transit from one pool to another. In most cases they seem to work satisfactorily, but unless they are well managed they can effect full use of the stream by the migrant fish. Alewives have their own crowd pressure and motion, their way of moving on, and any reduction in their numbers at any one time or counterpressure, keeping them back, may result in a decline because less will get to the ponds to spawn.

Fishways are more rigid than a natural stream bed, though sometimes less hazardous. Water levels change; the flow varies both in angle and pressure; and managers of a good fishway must be constantly on the alert for new conditions. A marked increase or decrease in the volume of water, especially as it is reflected at the head of a fish ladder, which usually has a gate or wooden dam of some kind, may create a barrier instead of an aid. Unless the adjustment in the dam is just right the head of water coming down may be almost impossible for a fish to surmount.

Alewives are not like the muscular west coast salmon with their spectacular leaps, as if shot by a giant sling. An alewife does not leap over a pool and up a falls so much as swim through it rapidly, being a much smaller fish and in smaller streams. If a head of water coming over a dam or sluice is at the wrong pitch, the fish will not be able to climb it. In designing a fishway an engineer has to take into account the relationship between the water head and the angle of the flow below it, which has to be translated into how far an alewife can swim at what speed.

A fish is supported by water—an advantage over cumbersome human beings in their own surrounding medium, the air—its specific gravity being close to that of its own body. The fish is so made as to swim through the water with as little resistance as possible. It also gets energy from the water, orienting itself by the current, or the various changes of pressure in the flow, the way a bird uses currents in the air. In so far as a bird is streamlined too, and finds in air pressure and weight the means to fly up and forward, their actions have something in common. A bird, like an alewife, may lose its momentum if the angle of climb gets too steep. Swimming and flying take place in fluid surroundings.

The difficulty in making an artificial aid like a fishway comes from the problem, in part, of understanding a fish's behavior; of meeting its needs; arranging its passage; trying, if not to control nature, at least to be a substitute for it. The positive results are plain to see, but there is something almost as elusive about it as trying to explain a fish in human language.

At one point along the Herring River in Harwich is a concrete fish ladder, twenty-five feet long and six feet wide. The pond above was high, after this same rainy spring, and the waters were roaring and frothing down. The alewives migrating upstream were being held back. Only a few I noticed were getting through. The flow had tremendous, deep force, so that the resting pools were not serving their function, and most of the fish that did manage by extraordinary effort to reach the head of water at the top were not able to pass it.

The racing torrent dropped to a wide, shallow basin which ended in the river winding on within its banks. A continuous long line of fish kept swimming through to the bottom of the ladder, where they would vainly skip and twist and strain through the water's force. Then they swung back in a semicircular arc across the basin and re-formed at its edge. There was a wide shiver on the water. They wheeled as in a dance, or like the planets in pursuit of light, where they ran up again into the flood. It happened time after time, in this futile but concurrent motion, a beauty to watch—its tension, effort, and relief were exactly co-ordinated with the water. These fish *were* the water. But I saw in them the mechanics of breath . . . contraction and expansion; and systole, diastole, balance and counterbalance, within the dynamics of all nature. They showed the push of life against a current, its running back and leaping forward, its fulfillment and defeat. It was the alewife circle again, as we have ours, in a motion of entirety; but almost impossible to translate.

"You never enjoy the world aright," wrote Thomas Traherne, "till the sea itself floweth in your veins." In the knowing and encompassing sense of his word *enjoy*, we will never know alewives until the motion, lift, light, weight, and changing beauty of the water is in some degree a part of us. In any case, we will never build the perfect fishway.

XIII
PERSISTENCE

When the little wire gate on the upper side of the seining pool was left open during the weekends the fish could pursue their destiny past the concession-aires. One weekday night during the last run in May some prankster took the gate out and caused much excitement in the alewives committee.

"Gawd! Gawd! . . . running all night long. Here's the town selling this young feller the fish, and he doesn't get any. We'll have to put a padlock on it . . ." etc. etc.

I may have had such a delinquent impulse my-self at one time, but I kept it way down.

There are two streams falling into the seining pool. Both start as pond outlets some fifty yards above, one with the fish ladder going down from it, and the other falling into a pool that ends above the old mill, the water of which can be used to run the water wheel on occasion by being diverted to a wooden sluiceway, instead of taking its natural course down over rocks into the seining pool. This second stream cannot be traveled by fish going up to spawn although they can go down it on their return journey.

One weekend I watched the fish at the top of the ladder as they jumped over the board dam, to meet at last the quiet stretch of pond water above it. The waters were growing green with algae as the season developed, and were penetrated by deep shadows, blue shafts from the sun, yellow and pink reflections from the spring leaves on the bank. Some were unable to make it and slipped back into the rushing, narrow flow in the ladder, and then tried again. Jumping the dam, they would give a final, vibrant, struggling push into the smooth, heavy weight of water over the rim and then shoot off, wriggling away, easing into a new peace. The impetus of this leap was enough to send some of them skittering along the flat surface on their sides, like skimmed stones. Others going into the pond would start back again toward the head of the ladder, and then return and wait a while as if they wanted company. As some new arrivals came they would swim a kind of half circle in relation to them, and then all would go on, having established a communication; but the general movement was a bolt into deeper water and then a rejoining into groups as they went on. After that, where do they go?

The Run

As far as fish migration in general is concerned
the spawning route beyond Stony Brook is not very
great. Roughly, the distance from the outlet through
Lower Mill Pond and Upper Mill Pond to the
end of Walker's Pond is about two and a quarter
miles. Upper Mill is the largest of these, being about
one and a half miles long and a quarter mile wide.
Where the fish spawn in this area is not too easy
to find out at first. Their preference as to spawning grounds seems to lie along stony, pebbly shores,
or shallow beaches. Many of them, before spawning, will travel to the farthest reaches of any given
water route. Others, depending perhaps on how far
the season is advanced and on their bodily development, will either go the entire distance and then
return part way, or spawn before they get there.

It may be that the earliest, coming in during the
month of March, or early April, when the pond
waters are still cold, will go farther than the later
arrivals. Their eggs develop more rapidly as the
temperature of the water advances, from around
the late forties say, at the beginning of the season,
to a maximum of 72 or 74 degrees. When the spawn
is not ready they may keep going, schooling, roaming in the ponds for days. But there are no hard-
and-fast rules about which of the alewife schools
goes where, and any generalizations would have
to be varied to suit conditions in other localities
where they are found. At one extreme they may
travel for six or eight miles up a tidal river, or at
another they may come into a pond connected with
salt water by a waterway or cut only a few feet long.

Many of them swim up headwaters as far as they
can go, through the last ditch to its stagnant end.
I have heard of their going through marshy land
in the direction of Pine Pond, a small pond beyond

Walker's, once connected with it I believe. There were cranberry bogs in this land, bordered by wire fences. The alewives would slip sideways under the wire so as to get to the other side. This is characteristic of them. When in very shallow water, inches deep, hardly enough for their bodies, they will skitter on, almost flat on their sides at times, going as far as they can until the water gets deeper.

Occasionally they have been known, on their way upstream, to butt their heads against a leaky dam where the flow of the water continued to come rather than go up a fishway to which it had been rerouted. (In one case an old log dam obstructing a stream had enough leaky cracks in it so that fish slithered through them). Such behavior may not make sense from our point of view, but it is part of a life necessity to them. Returning alewives are not concerned that we bypass a stream or send it off its course. They continue to follow the direction and limits of the flow that is in them, even as it might have been before we came.

Behind their persistence, if one term can encompass enough, is the "homing instinct." This is not only a matter of reacting to environmental waters, but insisting on that area where they were spawned, and where they grew, in the first few weeks or months before they migrated to salt water. In trying to rehabilitate the alewife population, men in fishery management are greatly helped by this powerful drive to return. Sometimes they are hindered by it.

There have been some areas in which the construction of dams across a stream or river has almost destroyed an old run, although there were a few fish left over, making a yearly, token migration. They continued to come in and spawn below

the last, impassable obstruction in their way; but
when the dams were abandoned and removed and
new fishways built so that they could travel upstream to the headwaters, the alewives stayed where
they were. They did not migrate beyond their original limit, and the population failed to increase.
It was as if there were an invisible wall in the water where the last, accustomed barrier had stood.
Not until the headwaters above were newly stocked
with spawning fish was there any chance of the run
being fully used.

This built-in reaction to home waters might go
back for thousands of years in an unobstructed
stream, or, in a new run, only three or four. It has
its limits, and its wisdom. What can go farther
back, or forward, than its own birth?

When I started watching the alewives I heard of
one phenomenon that seemed to me to surpass all
analysis. It tempted me to look for magic. The run
that comes up from Nantucket Sound on the south
side of the Cape by way of the Herring River goes
through a pond called Hinckley's, then through a
stream ending in a fairly large body of water called
Long Pond. The migrating alewives are also able
to go into another pond out of Hinckley's—north
of it, and east of Long Pond—called Seymour Pond,
but the majority seem to spawn in Long Pond,
from which there is only one clear exit. The fish
must go back to Hinckley's, the way they came.
But this outlet was not always the same. Early in
the nineteenth century the natural outlet was a
brook going into Seymour Pond, but it was blocked
and banked off by the construction of some cranberry bogs, and the present outlet was dug some
five hundred yards away. Now the extraordinary
thing is that on their return, the alewives still

school in the banked-up area of the old outlet. I
went over there and could find nothing to distin-
guish it from the rest of the sandy, water-lapped
shore, except that there was a slightly boggy area
on the other side of the road where the brook used
to run, and a trace of its route through the un-
derbrush.

Was there any reason at all why these fish should
be able to detect an old route cut off a hundred
years ago? The direction of its flow no longer existed
as currents in the water. Yet the "damfool herrin'"
were certainly behaving according to report. I
could see them, a school of several hundred, running freely along the shore, slipping lightly over
the sand through the unruffled pond waters. When
they reached the area of the old outlet they began
an almost puzzled circling, which continued for
some time before they swung back again. There
should have been a common-sense reason for it, but
I was tempted to ask, "What is verifiable truth?"
and not stay for an answer.

This story does not end in mysticism. It was suggested to me that there was a certain amount of
seepage at the outlet, probably going under the
bank and road, which the alewives felt and to
which they reacted. I can only say that all has not
been told about their sensitivity and perceptiveness
. . . transmitted from generation to generation
through thousands of years. I was quite sure at least
that they knew more about Long Pond than I.

Even if all the long-range problems about their
movements cannot be fathomed, there are enough
local ones to keep a searcher busy. Given enough
persistence of one's own, they may all be solved;
helped of course by the consistent fish. As the weeks
went by I learned about most of the local areas

where they spawned. I had noticed a school running offshore in the Upper Mill Pond, although I had not seen them in the act of spawning. But there was one place where I had seen them without knowing why. A few miles west of Stony Brook the fish come into the tidal inlet known as Quivett Creek, where they appear to reach a dead-end stretch of marsh ditched for mosquito control. I had tramped around in this boggy region, seen a few alewives there, and come to the quick conclusion that this was where they spawned. No one of whom I inquired in the vicinity could tell me otherwise. I did not know whether it was logical or not. They were not inclined, apparently, to spawn in the full ebb and flood of the tides, but looked instead for quiet waters. On the other hand, I had a pamphlet from the Fisheries Research Board of Canada which said, about alewives: ". . . in the Miramichi and other river systems extensive spawning takes place in the swift waters of the main tributaries." This was not swift water but it drained and flooded daily. However, the fish did not seem to stay long in the ditches, for whatever reason. It was hard to believe that they would return to the Bay so quickly, when they had come to spawn.

Being puzzled about it, I went back some days later. I walked again through the marsh at low tide when the ground was firmer, and finally I saw where the main flow narrowed into one of the ditches, then ran into a very small, almost imperceptible culvert that went under the highway, Route 6 A. Sure enough, on the other side of the road, in a ditched area tangled with briars, I could see many fish, slowly crowding on—but this was not the end of it either.

Beyond was an impenetrable tangle of woods and

thickets and an old abandoned house, reproachfully dying, with large empty eyes where the windows were, tall, unpainted, with dark-brown clapboards, and broken inside. You could reach this house from a side road off the highway. To one side of it was a small pond, which I had caught a glimpse of before, covered with water lilies in the summertime. I went in over a long high bank, part of an old road, that ran back of the house between the tangled ditches and the pond. There seemed to be no access from one side to the other; but toward the middle, on the side of the bank where the ditches ended, I saw a few alewives circling in a pool of still water. Then I heard a light splashing on the other side. I walked over through the thickets and saw a number of fish wiggling and thrashing up and over a little neck of water that ran out of the pond.

On one side this action, and on the other an apparently aimless moving through rocks and sodden branches in the water. Undoubtedly there was an old, hidden culvert that ran under the bank, but the underground passage must have been partly clogged and certainly very small. So the alewives that came into Quivett Creek spawned in that pond. Most of them had probably been hatched there. The flow from the sea had a logical termination. What else, the fish might ask me, had I expected?

XIV
SPAWNING:
THE DANCE

During the third week in May, when the run seemed about over I had still not seen them spawning, although I had heard a description of it from my local authority, Mr. Alexander.

"A kind of swish dance is what they do," said he, giving a hula-hula motion with his hands.

Harry also described them as sidling up at the shallow edges of the ponds, rocking as you would rock a baby; and then shooting out the spawn, their fins lifting up with the effort. The pond suckers, as he related it, would swim up to grab the eggs almost as soon as they came out of their bellies.

What about that school I had seen running along the shore of the Upper Mill Pond?

"Well, they were kind of getting acquainted, you know. Just cuddling together!"

This was on May 25, as I have it in my notes, and when I started out from the Herring Run to walk up to the ponds above it, Salvadore was still there with his truck, barrels, and net; but he said he was going to quit soon and deal in some redfish (another name for rosefish, or ocean perch). The redfish made tougher, better bait for lobsters anyway. While he had been in Brewster he had netted forty barrels a day on the average, sometimes as many as eighty, but he told me that he had not yet reached the four-hundred mark. One barrel, weighing some two hundred pounds, might contain around three hundred fish or more, so that about 120,000 alewives might be pulled out of Stony Brook in a season, though I imagine this is a very low estimate. I have heard it said that there are a potential two thousand barrels in the Brewster run during the full season, taking all fish. In an abundant year there might be close to six or seven hundred thousand adult alewives migrating up the brook. Even so, substracting the mortality, the necessary minimum of fish allowed through the gate during the week have a very heavy job to do to assure the return of hundreds of thousands of their race in three and four years' time.

Because of some kind of alewife caution or deliberation, not enough of them were going into the seining pool to make a good haul. They were delaying on the down side of the road. Salvadore waded in with his rubber boots on to drive them under and through the bridge, but they hardly budged, so he crouched down with little more than three feet

of height for body room, and swashed in after them.
They skittered before him, landing with a simultaneous series of quick dashes into the pool.

It was a warm day. There was a new lassitude
in the air, and the sweet smell of lilacs. The gulls
were gone that had flocked in quarreling and
screaming when the run was heaviest, hovering and
rising over the waters and their hordes of fish, bold
enough sometimes to perch on the bridge over the
run, looking very large, with their pale-yellow eyes
glaring as naked as stone.

Once I saw a herring gull display its fantastic
eating capacity by dropping down into the fish
ladder, grabbing an alewife, and swallowing it
whole. Down went the fat, foot-long fish in a few
gulps, headfirst so that neither scales nor sawbelly
would stop the progress. Then the loaded gull flew
very heavily away as I came up, the alewife's tail
having barely disappeared.

Now, in place of gulls, there were a few dove-
gray, black and white quawks perched on the
outer branches of overhanging trees like heavy
sculptured ornaments, or standing in the water
with their spearhead bills ready poised for a frog
or small fish. I have heard it said, incidentally, that
these night herons keep the gulls away. I have never
witnessed any aggressive action between the two
races. On the whole they seem to respect each
other's territory and to keep their distance from
each other; but I have seen quawks and gulls together waiting for little alewives on the flats beyond Paine's Creek.

In the brook there were still some fish ascending,
but many more were going back. It is a little hard
to tell the difference at first, since both face up
against the current, but the returning alewives

gradually drop back, and many of them have the characteristic white marks on them of fresh-water fungus infection. The strain of spawning and using up their store of fat makes them thin, slow, and weary. They have lost a good deal of their vigor, though not to the extent of preventing the return journey.

In spite of this "spring fever" day it was not that the greatness of events was over . . . only the first great toppling of a wave, only the first violent forwardness with its illimitable sounds and changes. There was a steadier greenness on the trees, and blossoms on the high lilacs. The run waters went on with a constant wail and wah, if without the turbulence of a few weeks earlier. I left the Herring Run and walked up into the warm pine woods to try and find the culminative point of the migration.

A light wind was running straight down the long surfaces of the Upper Mill Pond when I reached it, and little waves scudded ahead. I walked on the north side where sandy banks descended to the shore, shaded by pitch pines and covered with viburnum bushes and bearberry, a pink-blossomed, shiny-leaved ground cover locally known as "hog cranberry." There were stretches of amber sand, small stones, or gravel, along the pond's edge. A fat sucker jumped for a fly and crashed heavily back into the water.

All at once I heard a light thrashing and noticed a large water snake under a blueberry bush. It had dropped a small salamander that was twisting over and over on the ground, its damp body collecting bits and shreds of dry leaves. As I came up, the snake hung over a low-lying branch and watched me, its mouth slightly open with a little toothed white and pink jawline showing. I picked up the salamander and dropped it into the pond, where it hesitated for a few seconds and then wiggled away into a patch of green ooze and deeper water. With a stick, I tossed the snake twenty feet away, thus establishing myself as universal arbitrator.

As I walked and watched along the shore I saw one group of alewives, and then another, running by, looking light-colored and bright in the sunny water. Sometimes these groups seemed to be made up of one female escorted by several males, but the closer they came to shore the more intermingled they were, and it was not clear to me that this was a definite pattern. When she is running upstream, the female's eggs are unripe, but ripen soon after arrival in the ponds, provided the water temperature is high enough—between 55 and 60 degrees may be the average spawning temperature during the big April and early May runs. As to the act of spawning, the female, depending on her size, deposits anywhere between sixty thousand and a hundred thousand eggs (each some 0.05 inches in diameter) in shallow places; and because they are sticky they adhere to gravel, sticks, stones, or whatever they settle on. The males, who have been following the females closely, immediately cover the eggs with milt, thrashing and scattering it with their tails. The eggs hatch out in some six days' time when the water is at 60 degrees, and in three days or less at 72.

When I first watched them spawn I saw a group of alewives run, circle, and weave offshore, sometimes slowing up at deeper holes on the bottom, or behind rock-protected water, and then come in close, with one quick impulse. They raced in to-

gether to the gravelly, shallow edge, through water
not much more than ankle deep, with a sinewy,
rippling motion. Then in the shadows under an
overhanging shrub there was a flipping, whirling,
and thrashing, a breaking of the surface. The female slapped up against the side of a rock with a
rising, shuddering motion of the body as though it
were shaking everything out of it, while the others
simultaneously writhed, coiled, thrashed tails, and
shimmered through. Then it seemed to me that
there were a few seconds in which they slowly re-
assembled their senses to go elsewhere. The word
"deposit" was hardly active enough.

A fat pond sucker was hanging around the center of activity, following the alewives slowly like
a small sunken log. It was obvious that eggs, to
this crude, crass, lazy taster of a fish, were the ulti-
mate delicacy.

There were other occasions when the alewives,
in greater numbers, swam next to the shore, spawning in what might have been concentric groups for
several hundred yards. Some at the edge would be
coiling and thrashing while others swam on or
circled back. The fish that were farther out in the
pond ran nervously, with eager movements, making
quick turns as if reconnoitering, or practicing for
a culminating turn. They collected suddenly when
spawning, with quick, spontaneous decision. I noticed that the males while running in would often
shoulder or press the females on. The characteristic
thrashing whirl they make is sudden and amazing,
almost like a pinwheel in a short burst.

Their attendants, the pond suckers, would loll
in the slow rock of the pond waters. They are large,
soft-looking fish, with round, pink fins, and white,
fleshly lower lips with which they go nibbling and

nuzzling with snail-like speed over the bottom. The alewives by contrast are small, gray, and quick. If alewife eggs are deposited between rocks the suckers go down in after them, and, if the water is shallow enough, present the odd picture of a large top-heavy body sticking down with its tail above the surface.

It is not I think, incongruous to apply the word love to a cold-blooded fish. In this spawning act there is an imperative rhythm, with grace in its preparation and power in its fulfillment.

Sometimes the war cry of gulls, in small flocks settling on the shore waters or rising up, told me where the alewives were, but most of the time I found them in accustomed places like that stretch of shore on the Upper Mill Pond. Sometimes I could hear them splashing before I saw them. They seemed to be more inclined to spawn when the water was not too rough. On the other hand, I watched them spawning when the ponds were very choppy and the small waves were pushing them as they thrashed at the edge. Once, on the south side of the pond, I noticed the suckers before the alewives. There were twenty or more lined up as if they were giving the bottom a slow going over. When groups of alewives ran in and characteristically heaved, flipped, and writhed at the edge, the big suckers would move up closer. They were so oblivious to anything but their slow gluttony that I could tap them on the head with a stick.

Occasionally a couple of alewives would give a sucker a little rush, a brief chase, as much, so it looked, by way of sport as aggressiveness. They were certainly incapable of damaging it very much, and it could not be driven away for long. An over-doze of suckers in any one area seemed to discourage the alewives a little and make them move on, but on the whole they too were so intent on what they were doing that they hardly noticed anything else. They had to fulfill themselves; then, stunned, go on. The eggs were expendable.

XV
THE RETURN

After the first week in June there were very few if any alewives coming up over the dam at the head of the run. An increasing number, on the other hand, were going down, and I could find very few in the ponds. I was to see them returning well on in July, which indicates that while many, perhaps a majority, will leave the ponds a few days or a week after spawning, others may stay there for weeks longer. For reasons known only to the individual fish, occasional strays have been found lingering in fresh water well into the winter.

On the morning of June 10, after a lapse of a

few days in which I had seen only a few returning,
a boy who was weekending on the Upper Mill Pond
told me he had seen thousands go by in the direction of the Herring Run. So they were still schooling for the return to salt water, progressing again
by accumulative motion. In a few weeks some of
the little ones, hatched out earlier, would start
down too.

I stood on a rock and looked down into the water along that peaceful stretch above the dam.
This is an area where Indians gathered and
camped when the alewives were running, spearing
them, or taking them with nets made out of reeds.
Many Indian artifacts have been found on the surrounding slopes. On this June day insects were settling down on the still surface. A shower was due—
the air heavy. An alewife slanted slowly up to the
surface and then dropped down again. It left a perfect circle behind it that gently widened over the
blended images of clouds, leaves, and rocks. Then
as other small circles, raindrops falling, began to
show on the water, a belt of flying herons passed
in reflection. A breeze corrugated the surface
slightly and the fish swam slowly on toward the
roar of the seaward-casting falls.

The returning migrants now have a choice between two outlets: one at the top of the fish ladder,
and the other at a board dam where the water
drops into a long pool above the old mill. At the
far end of the pool the waters fall again a short
but precipitous distance, often roaring full and
hard down the rocky slope into the seining pool.
The alewives use both outlets, but the majority
seem to prefer the falling second stream to the
ladder by which they came up, perhaps because it
is the point of greatest flow. Where they drop down

over the falls it looks to the proportionate, or dis-
proportionate, senses of a human being almost
suicidal. Most go over tail first. Then they appear
to be dashed headlong down the jagged incline that
ends in rocky narrows going off at an angle to the
pool. One after another they flip and fall, their
bodies bent like bows, and flash finally, swift and
vibrant—not, surprisingly, having been broken to
pieces—at the bottom. Occasionally a fish near the
end of the slope will frantically try to skitter back
up. Presumably it is trying to reduce the speed at
which the ground is going by it, in the way a man
tries to brake himself when running downhill. But
this almost helter-skelter falling reveals almost as
much of the alewife's supple strength as its leaping
up against the current.

As June went on and polliwogs turned to frogs,
the leaves came fully out, clover and buttercups
were blooming, and the pond algae had increased
at a fast rate so that a thick green scum gathered
behind the dam, and the pond waters were yellow-
green. Still you could see the fish gathering at in-
tervals massed sometimes fifty feet or more behind
the two outlets. There is a small wooden foot-
bridge over the board dam at the head of the pool.
When I lay down on the bridge and looked under
at the curved lip of the water I could see the fish
gathering behind. Against the steady rush and
whine I could hear a dull, deep change in sound
as the fish suddenly turned and plummeted over.
Their bodies, enlarged behind a green curve of
water, had a metallic sheen, a dull silver, as they
would wheel in, loom up, and drop away. I came
back at night, and could still hear that heavy sound
in this lens, or gong, of water.

In each new phase of migrant action there is an

old ceremony. The alewives approach the dam, in groups of varying sizes. They circle, withdraw, and swim back again. Some of them swim between the two outlets as if to decide which one to take. Coming closer, they show an increasing animation, a quicker circling and flipping, as if the outward pull of the water resulted in a more vital excitement between them. After many more starts and withdrawals, lasting anywhere from fifteen minutes to an hour or more from the approach of a given group, or school—using that term in the sense of larger numbers—one or more fish will drop over, and then the rest will follow.

I watched one school making these ceremonious retreats and approaches for two hours. When they finally started dropping over I counted some fifty fish a minute for about fifty-five minutes, until there were only three left. This remaining three must have lacked the common stimulus to go, the rhythm of sufficient numbers, and they stayed behind, as more fish began to draw in closer from the pond. I have seen this often. Sometimes seven, nine, and up makes enough of a group to start over on its own; very occasionally one alewife will go it alone; but it does seem as if a certain variable minimum will not take the move upon itself.

Though a single fish may be the first to go over, or to advance upstream, it is hard, from my observation, to attribute any leadership to individuals, male or female. The crowd provides its own pressure and momentum. Perhaps the circling of these groups and schools, and their dropping over, might be analogous, though it is a looser motion, to a flock of sandpipers flying off simultaneously as if they were cast out by a lithe, invisible wire, and then turning on an instant, glinting in the sun.

The impulse is in the rhythmic unity of the group, even though in the case of the fish some may be left off or behind until they are rejoined in it.

The speed at which they drop over seems to depend on the size and pressure of the oncoming school—population pressure, in other words, unless pressure of numbers is a better term, which must also affect the timing of their entry from the sea. Sometimes they go over: one—two—three—four—one a second; but if the group is small the rate may be ten to twenty a minute. Finally there are those few fish left behind that circle around at the outlet or turn back into deeper water where another school will be coming up.

All morning, as the alewives massed, circled, and dropped, there was one fish that kept wandering through and over the others in a puzzling way. It was a conspicuously darker color, which is characteristic of blindness, as I learned later on. Its loss of sight, then, had deprived it to some degree of the community action, though it had been able to feel its way toward the outlet. Occasionally one that looked exceptionally tired and slow would drop over the falls by itself. I noticed also that those which were scarred and infected seemed to have lost some of the fire of communication.

To the casual eye the spent fish may not look any thinner or weaker than the rest, though when they hit the seining pool they are obviously in no hurry to move on, but circle slowly around it for some time. Their flesh, for the human carnivore, is of poorer quality than when they came in from salt water. Going back to history again, it seems that the recipients of alewives in the Caribbeans were not always pleased with the product. There were complaints in the eighteenth century, as I have indicated, and in the early nineteenth as well, when plantation owners in the West Indies objected that this food was doing bad things to their slaves. They said that alewives taken when they were going downriver after spawning were "poison fish," and "the very worst food that can be given to slaves, as it both disheartens them, keeps them continually murmuring, and brings on those scorbutic diseases so common among negroes in that climate."

Bad food or not, they were in all things directional, with the water and the season, moving on and out, taking the rhythms of perpetuation with them, these "reflex machines," bearers of strong tides. They had been giving me something of a lesson in cosmic weather, though I was still a hopeless beginner. From one place, one road, around one circle, they had led me through so much variety that I was left to wonder at my omissions. The man-made world must still have far to go to learn its inner and outer relations to a greater, expanding world of lives that are given, not made.

What further connections are there, say, between the sun and sight, between our tactile senses and the medium of earth and air in which we are born, between the moon and the tides and the rhythms of water and of blood? Who knows more about the universe—I with my conscious measurements, my personal faltering, or the poor fish with its unthinking precision through the various unknown? Can we not combine? In any case, whatever human beings decide about what is effective or ineffective, what shall stay or what shall go, the alewives know where they live.

The crowd in the seining pool moved slowly, in a wide circle around its rim. Most of their inland enemies had gone now. The human hunters had driven away. The herring gulls had flown to other feeding grounds. Not that one enemy or another made much difference to them, except in terms of sudden fear. Like their eggs, they were expendable. Nature's ruthlessness, the using and the building up of that which fed and that which was food, would keep them on the way of primordial energy. For the same reason they were also spenders—one of the great sacrificial coinages of the living world.

Still this point in their migration before the return to salt water might be called a place of demobilization, a separation center. They swam slowly around in the pool, passing between each other, but always a part of the circle, each fish with its body and its large black eyes leading forward, obedient to it. They dispersed very gradually throughout the day. One small group after another broke off, sparks from a wheel, and the fish let themselves be carried back down the brook where the outlet of the pool led under the road. In the run below where they went back step by step to the sea—whose pull was in them—they faced up against the current, their orientation, with a tired, slow weaving. I noticed a little perch attendant on them. It ran down backward with the large procession, giving the alewives a look of ceremonial grandeur. I have seen sunfish join up too, although there could be a point on the approach to brackish water when they decide that home life is better than parades. These motions must be catching, communicating to other lives and races than those in which they originate. All have their way stations, or orbits, along a route that is being followed out with primal grace and power.

XVI
THE YOUNG
FOLLOW AFTER

When the last adult alewife of the season drops down Stony Brook for the tidal inlet and the sea, it has left the renewal of its continuity and motion behind it. The little alewives follow out the route of their elders with a silent animism, sent by ancient habit and unknown need. The repetitive ways of the anadromous fish come out of geologic time. On the long track since then, the adults, reaching their spawning grounds, have had the drive of the sperm toward the egg. From the top of a falls to the depth of the sea there are equivalent lifts and falls in their own being. The young, tiny and perishable though they may be, have the same inalienable motion in them.

After hatching, young alewives form dense schools, and begin to feed on the plankton—tiny organisms and plant life—in the pond waters. Occasionally they can be seen flipping on the surface. They are subject to attack by all kinds of predators: perch, pickerel, frogs, herons, kingfishers, water snakes, and many others, from the time they are out of the egg. Landlocked waters are often stocked with spawning alewives for that very reason. The fry make an excellent diet for such popular game fish as bass, trout, and salmon.

The survivors begin to move out of the ponds about the beginning of July. In other areas I have heard that the majority do not start down until September. The first time I saw them was on the second of July, when they were being drawn down by the thousands through the dam opening at the head of the fishway. They were scarcely over an inch long, and as they came in from the ponds they reflected the summergreen of the water. Their eyes seemed huge in proportion to the size of their bodies. They were poured down the boiling water of the ladder, tossed around like chips and slivers, spilled down helter-skelter; but where the current slowed, farther down the brook, they held together in the fashion of their race.

There is an account, in a *Report of the Alewife Fisheries of Massachusetts*, 1921, of some alewives hatched out in the fisheries at Sandwich, Massachusetts, in June of 1919. The eggs were put in water of 72 degrees Fahrenheit and half of the lot, in that warm temperature, were hatched in only forty-eight hours. "In the surface water were thousands of tiny alewives with food sacs nearly transparent in appearance, and with tails resembling fine silk threads. The tiny creatures, about one-fifth of an inch in length, wiggled through the water with surprising activity. The eyes in both the egg and the hatched fish were but faintly visible. At the end of ninety-six hours their size had increased considerably, the outline of the yolk sac and the body was plainly marked, and the eyes showed prominently. By this time all the eggs had hatched. In cold water the period of development is retarded proportionately to the lowering of the temperature."

In a month the young alewives were about three-fifths of an inch long and by autumn between two and four inches. At three-fifths of an inch they look more like a sand eel than an alewife—an observation quoted in the same report. When they are an inch and a fifth long they look more like the adults. Their bodies are shorter at the size and they have a large head and relatively large eyes. When they reach one and two-fifths inches, about the size of those I saw, they look much the same, but with the addition of the alewife's sawbelly—"serrations of the middle abdominal scales."

It may be that in times past little alewives have been unable to migrate out of the waters in which they were hatched, and local races of a landlocked variety were established. The landlocked alewives are much dwarfed in comparison with the salt-water variety. Some years ago there were a number of complaints from householders in New York City that small fish were coming out of the faucets. The Deputy Commissioner of the Department of Water Supply, Gas and Electricity, referred the matter to the New York Aquarium, which investigated and found that these were none other than landlocked alewives: *Pomolobus pseudoharengus.* They had been spawned in the Kensico Reservoir, and in the autumn they passed through the ⅝-inch mesh of the screens at the outlet. This might suggest the migrating habit of their ocean cousins. A friend of mine, getting the parent stream theory turned around, speculated as to whether a study might not show them returning from the same faucets over a period of years!

But no conclusive evidence was found that these fish were following out any consistent migration. For a period of eight years during the course of the survey hardly any fish were reported as dropping into the kitchen sinks of New York.

One interesting thing about the landlocked alewives is that they are subject to mass mortalities, or "die offs," for reasons yet undecided. In some areas, like Cayuga Lake in New York State, this happens occasionally, but in others, Lake Ontario, for example, fairly regularly. This does not necessarily happen after spawning, so invites no analogy to the west coast salmon. Many of the dead fish have not yet reached sexual maturity.

As to the normal, coastal migration of the fry from fresh to salt water, why do they leave when they do? Is there any theory that can account for these little fish suddenly moving out of the waters in which they were born, so rich with the freshwater food that gave them their initial growth? Are they fleeing their enemies? Yet the young of the fresh-water fish are preyed upon too, and they stay behind.

There is an explanation about salmon fry which has them gradually going seaward in order to escape the brighter light in the shallow fresh waters;

but is there anything in the constitution of an alewife that is not accustomed to sunlit waters? They do not escape them so much as seek them, because of their warmer temperature. Aside from that, I would think, from my own observation, and the comments of others, that they have no preference between the dark and light along their way—they run through both—but do not like a sudden change. For example, they waited all one morning before coming out of the shaded waters under Stony Brook Road to go into the brightness of the seining pool, only moving when a shadow fell across it that was cast by the old mill.

If the adults swim toward the coast in the spring because of some change in their make-up consonant with changes in the waters where they swim, is there also some change in food and temperature which makes the young start to leave fresh water at a particular time? The little alewives are creatures of such sensitivity to their medium, to its changes, and to what they eat, that a factor in the timing of their migration might be some internal discomfort, or so it was suggested to me. To begin to find out, a scientist would have to follow all the stages of a little alewife's birth and growth, tracing where it goes, what it eats, and what the temperature, depth, and density of the water is along the way. He would also have to do this for every age group that leaves the three ponds from July through October, analyzed pond by pond, since conditions differ in each one. During this period the little fish leave at all stages in the seasonal development of the ponds, while not all of one age group seem to go with the others. Many appear to stay in the ponds for several months. So attempting consistency with such findings might result in more indigestion for the investigator than the fish themselves.

From the outward evidence all I can say is that these little ones do not start schooling to move out of the ponds until they are over an inch in length. I have seen them, still not much more than pin size, circling a few hundred yards above the outlet, but neither swimming with the flow nor letting themselves be drifted on. Logically then, the point at which they are stimulated to leave must coincide with growth, the rate of which depends on food and temperature in the ponds.

Warm-water ponds are more favorable to growth than cold-water ponds. They turn out better fish, larger and healthier. By the same token a cold spring and summer will result in a poorer crop of alewives. They will probably be hatched later. The colder pond waters will bring down the "plankton bloom," in other words less food for the fish. As a result, young alewives going to salt water that year will be smaller, weaker, more subject to disease, and less able to escape their enemies.

It is just possible, then, that some spring when the annual run of alewives is smaller than usual, for no apparent reason, you might find an answer to the mystery in a cold season, four years before.

After the first young alewives have moved out, having attained the size and response necessary for it, you can see a gradual increase in size from early summer until autumn. One of the unsolved questions is why the earliest to go will not stay longer in the ponds. Why not relax, if a fish can, and eat well until autumn, as in fact large numbers of them do. Were they nearest the outlet? Perhaps the larger fish that begin to appear later on were hatched

earlier and therefore came from farther back in the chain of ponds.

Of course there is nothing rigid about their time-table, nothing exact about their migratory behavior. Whatever stimulates it, their new momentum takes the form of a gradual circling out. I have heard that in some areas they will start down and then return when they can swim back up the outlet, if the force of the water is not too strong for them. They may be in a state of indecisive action for a while, or so it sounds, but most of them are moved to go at some time before winter sets in, though there have been many exceptions to the rule. John Burns, of the Massachusetts Division of Marine Fisheries, tells me that he saw a "generous school of fry" one January, coming down under the ice of a frozen pond at Bournedale.

Perhaps this phenomenon of migration in the young fish is not susceptible of final analysis. Might that be because it is so simple, however complex in detail and circumstance, simple though intangible in the life rhythm it embodies? However slow or fast their response to it may be, the little fish must be obeying an organic, directional drive that goes back beyond history. As a part of their growing up they may develop the same kind of built-in response to the waters in which they find themselves as their parents schooling offshore in the spring; and they come to have an intercommunication that knows its way. It is not the adult call of sexual maturity that moves them, and yet they must have a biological need to start out together on the same living track.

I recognize how much an amateur may leave out of his calculations, and only proffer my individual guess that they follow the outward flow of the

ponds when they grow to feel a rhythmic, habitual
motion in them that responds to it and that belongs
in its balance to the whole race of alewives between land and sea. The fresh-water minnows stay
where they are, no matter how hard the pull of
the waters may be. I have seen them lazing in the
shallows while a school of little alewives darted
over them, restlessly moving on. And as I followed
the young migrants I saw in them a roaming, roving sweep like sea birds made for distant journeys.

I watched them coming down from July through
October and into November, from the lush green of
early summer to the red and brown of dry weeks
in August, and on to the cool days of autumn when
the sea turned a brighter blue and winds and clouds
blew full—all the way almost to the hardening in
of winter and its sullen skies. The alewife is a part
of the life of Stony Brook and the ponds above it
for at least seven months out of the year. And the
fact that so many return again to the particularity, the uniqueness of these waters is a reminder of
the power of living form and place together, the
welding of those strands of near and far in the body
of a fish, the body of the world. The fish egg rolls
around on a greater axis than its own.

So the first of the tiny fish came down by the
thousands during the first week in July. After that
there was hardly a day until the middle of August
when there were not at least a few to be seen in the
brook. Gradually they grew larger, so that in August they were up to two inches on the average.
The next big movement, after an August lull, began on September 6 and 7. Their size by then had
increased to between two and two and one-half
inches. A few were considerably larger. I measured
one at the surprising length of four and one-half

inches, and another, which escaped my net, looked to be well over five.

It was easy enough to get a sampling, because they had a tendency, owing to their very light weight perhaps, to be caught at the bottom of the little falls that poured out of each resting pool in the ladder. They were tossed, turned, tumbled in the bubbling water, flung out from it but returning to be tossed again. On the surface of that turbulence they sometimes managed like gulls riding drafts of wind, but then they would drop down and under and be carried off to the edge once more. This would go on for a long time, although they were very gradually dropping down the brook. Because of this tendency of theirs I was able to scoop them out of the falls with a sieve—although the larger they were the more elusive.

I noticed their absence during a number of cloudy and rainy days in September and their return when the sun shone; which is not to say that I did not see them on overcast days too, but the good days started them going. They responded to warmth like the adults. Beginning in October the next schools of fish coming down had increased in size, so that the average seemed to have gone up to about two and three-quarters to three inches. This movement, off and on, kept up until the end of the month. I saw one last small group coming in to the upper falls on November 16.

In the larger individuals I noticed a wider radius of response, even though they circled with fish much smaller than themselves. They were faster. They were gaining more control, and more apparent ability to see what was coming, my hand or sieve, for example, and to avoid it. These later age groups were not tossed downstream 'so helplessly as the earlier one-and-a-half-inchers had been. They showed more strength against the current. Yet the motion of them all was consistent with what I had seen in the adults going the same course.

I would see a little gray school of fish circling above the dam between the two outlets, with a beautiful, light swinging, and running by. There might be a sudden split in the middle of them when a leaf fell or a dragonfly touched close to the surface of the water. Then one or two of the tiny fish would fall back over the outlet with an almost electric beat, while the rest stayed. Then four or five more dropped over, and suddenly all the rest spilled over after them. They were tumbled down the first steep ladder; then they followed out the longer stretches farther on, sometimes running with the current, sometimes turning back against it; and on the down side of the road they were caught in the in-boiling waters of the second fishway, before the uninterrupted flow ahead.

A minority came down the side or waste stream instead of swimming down the second fishway, and, because they were not contained there as they were in the resting pools, I could see more clearly what happened to them as they approached a falls. The current was consistently smooth and swift, but it was a long, level, calm stretch of water. I watched them swimming straight down with it and then, quite close to the sudden tug of the high falls, they would turn back. They felt it, and had a quick response to it. It was as though they suddenly had their equilibrium tested, and that they were like trapeze artists feeling wrists, body, and rope, before swinging out and over.

Then down where Stony Brook was broad, shallow, and swift, they ran, or were carried on, like sticks and leaves. Where the water lost some of its force they swam up against it, in little schools together, or they swam off to the side of the main flow for a while, sometimes lingering in deeper water, or the shelter of rocks and banks, but continually returning to it, always a part of that outward seagoing rhythm. Gradually they traversed the swirling, eddying, longstretching waters. They moved toward the influence of the tides where the brook ran through the marshes. They held position or circled back when the brackish water came in against them. Finally they swam, or were pulled out, from Paine's Creek on an ebb tide, and moved toward the new shelter of the sea and its many dangers.

XVII
THE POWER
OF FRAGILITY

I think one of the greatest challenges is to watch each bounded living thing with care for its particularity, as far as we can go, to find out we can go no farther. Flower, fish or leaf, child or man— they take none of our suggestions as to rules. Each has a strong language that we never quite learn. No matter how many times I try to describe the alewife by the uses of human speech, or classify its habits, its intrinsic perfection resists me. It is *something else*. It goes on defying my own inquiring sense of mystery.

The beauty of a little alewife held between the

fingers, struggling out of water, dying, by human arbitrary reach, becomes the subject of thought and language, creative protestation in themselves. But the two-inch creature makes a mightier protest than my conscious sight of it . . . wild, fragile, vibrant, shivering with a quickness that will die out in a matter of seconds. It is a marvelously knit animal, compact, flexible, shining, with its tiny meshed scales that interlock the light, iridescent silver like the adults, green, yellow, purple, receiving earth and sky. And the eyes, wholly black, interminably deep. By a chance scoop of my hand it is out in the long killing air, the little vibrancy out with the bird-gray clouds, a leashed arrow straining for the stars, that have their running too in the circle of immensity.

Fragile they are, and powerful, a wonderful work of which so many are made as to afford them death as well as life. Let us say, arbitrarily, that 150,000 female alewives lay their eggs in the ponds above Stony Brook each year. After the pond suckers take their share and the remaining eggs hatch out, then the young alewives run the gauntlet of their first few days and weeks of life. The toll taken would seem incredible if it were not also natural and expected. From billions the young are reduced to millions.

If a run is to keep up over the years, there has to be an annual survival, or "escapement," of somewhere between 3 and 7 per cent. Say a hundred million hatched, out of the original nine billion eggs. Five percent of that, or five million, have to reach salt water in order to assure a normal spawning migration in three or four years' time. From that figure, of course, you subtract the alewife mortality during their years of growth in the sea. I claim nothing for my calculations, but, rough as they are, they may help to indicate how much potential goes into the end result.

It is not only the alewives that are provided for by these great numbers, but the predators which hunt them. The alewives are only part of a great complex of need. Sometimes I have watched the fry as they swam out across the Brewster flats on an ebb tide, running in shallow water from the mouth of Paine's Creek. In September, before they have migrated south, crowds of terns, along with the resident herring gulls and ring-billed gulls, would be hovering over the water and diving or flocking in as the alewives appeared. I watched the constant, sinewy beat of their wings as they held against a west wind. The sky was swept way up with long cirrus clouds. The young alewives were running into death and beyond it, in a windy world that teemed with risk and creation.

A friend of mine, who worked in the vicinity some years ago, watched the tiny fish coming down above the old mill one autumn day. He saw some night herons standing in the lip of the dam gobbling the "poor little devils" up as they went over. He was amazed at their stomach capacity. Then he noticed that at the rocky falls where the pool ended above the water wheel and seining pool only a few were dropping over as compared to the thousands coming in from the pond, and the toll the quawks took did not account for it. Somehow, somewhere, in this short stretch of water, they were disappearing into a gulf, or, more properly, a maw. It didn't seem right. It made him angry, although: "You can't get mad at nature because that's the way it is." He got a hook and line, baited it, threw it into the pool; and in two hours he had fished out seventy-six eels.

These slithering, hoselike creatures are still there in season waiting to prey on the fish. It does not take long as a rule to see one coming up at the edge of the bank, though I have never seen them in any great quantity, because they usually lie hidden in the muddy bottom. Sometimes you can see a small group of eels of varying sizes in one of the resting pools of the fishway below the road, where the little alewives as they go down must almost fall into their mouths. With broad-ribboned tails on one end of their long-finned bodies and pointed snouts on the other, they weave and flip over, arch and float in the water. Partly because of the narrow space, and their tendency to stay or be caught in the turbulent pools, many of the little fish cannot avoid being eaten. They have only the safety of numbers.

Having developed a certain affection for the race by this time, I must say I had feelings of pity for these little ones, helplessly tossed in and out of death. They *are* fragile, like the young of other animals. They will not last more than about three-quarters of a minute out of water. But they are not ones to know or care whether I think of them or not. They are parts of a great ordered hunger, and a vast provision for things. They are both victims and executioners, the feeders and the fed upon, in the intercommunication of every single plant and animal in the natural world. There is nothing for affection in that order perhaps, unless we conceive of it in terms of love as well as annihilation.

I have followed them out and seen where their consistent motion, their automatic reaction to the waters they swim in, has brought them to grief. It serves for survival and also for disaster. When the young alewives get out to salt water on an ebb tide, they are not able to calculate how long it will last, or so we presume, and whether they should move out soon or stay behind. The result is that many are left stranded and wildly skittering in the rivulets that thread the sandy flats at extreme low tide. From the time the outgoing waters of Paine's Creek begin to get low, they are also subject to attack by crowds of herons and gulls—but supposing they survive that and still have a chance in a matter of an hour or an hour and a half to reach deeper water? It is very often the case that because of their habit of heading back against the current they delay too long and lose their chance of escape. They are caught high and dry on the sand or in water so shallow that they are unable to move on, and so are easy prey for the birds. I have followed them through low water and seen them turn back, just as they had a chance to follow one waning current to join another and so out to safety; but when I use the word safety I have to remind myself that the flow goes where it will.

Now it is possible that you might interpret this behavior as a reluctance to leave the inland waters. They have a drive in them to go to salt water eventually, but they may be in no hurry. In some areas they stay in estuaries or tributaries for a long time. At Paine's Creek and the channel above it they may have no alternative but to be carried out on the ebb tide.

When they finally reach Cape Cod Bay they probably school in fairly shallow shoal areas where the water is warmest, inviting bass or bluefish of course, to "come and get it."

"Shiners" some call them, confusing alewife fry with fresh-water shiners, of which there are a great many species, but shine they do. In the summer at low tide the bathers try to catch them with their hands, or jump after them where they glitter in the pools. Sometimes there are trails of the little fish left behind by those gluttons the gulls. In death they look frail, limp, almost diaphanous. No longer so reflecting and vibrant, their bodies are a pale silver-white like the underside of fallen poplar leaves. Some of the heads are left uneaten along with the headless bodies strewn in the rivulets along the ridged sands. Sometimes their bodies are ripped down, gashed, leaving raw stripes on them. These wounds look no less cruel and vivid because of their tiny size.

XVIII
GOING OUT

The first alewife I saw in early spring was wild and new to me, feeling its way upcurrent alone, cautiously, as if testing out an old trail. Down Stony Brook there were long patterns in the water dappled like fish scales. In the sky above there were cloud tosses and wind turns during a break toward spring that the fish itself exemplified. Later on the fry in the apparently indiscriminate times they moved out and headed for salt water seemed to be pulled as if by moon tides and turning earth. The course I followed was full of natural complexity. Forms and patterns were endlessly co-ordinate and suggestive, but with the mystery of their making, the universal power, at once ordered, vast, fluid, out of reach.

The alewife migration taught me how to start. Had we been two and a half miles up from salt water to the farthest pond, then back again, or was it three thousand? I had learned that measurement was indefinite.

I still knew next to nothing about their lives in salt water. And what was ahead on land? I could expect them to follow certain rules of behavior. They would come back year after year unless the run was so consistently overfished that the population dwindled. I knew where to look for them now, and had some acquaintance with laws of supply and demand, plus the effects of management or the lack of it. Perhaps alewives could be expected in general to do what they had done before. But those laws that lead all migrants on have more in store for us than we can anticipate. The variations I had found in action and circumstance, following those fish, variations like the changes of air and water, leaves, grass and ground, intermoving light and shadow, were unexpected and perpetual. If the alewives ever proved that anything was static, it could only have been in me. There is no personifying the unknown fish. I am not acquainted with it yet; but now we are on a run together.

The alewife is another of the amplifications and extensions of life. In the flip of its body, its communicable "Let's go," if offers to be followed. So that race with its recoil and approach, approach and recoil, circling in consonance with the forces of the earth has the lesson of migration in ourselves. When I watched them coming in on their old, persistent track and felt so much in my own senses of that exploring, through the growing and falling off of leaves, the wind charging and easing off, the bright waters, I knew there was an infinite sum in me of the unused. What *is* migration? Is it to "pass from one place to another"—just that? And its causes may be the need for food or to reproduce in season; but surely the term comprises a great deal more.

Whether the migration of animals seems random, or with definite intent, it leads across the earth. All the studies made of individual species result in new directions to be explored, new unknowns about the actions of other lives, and the ways they follow. The mystery about the travels of birds, eels, monarch butterflies, or alewives, is not only a matter of routes or seasonal behavior. It has to do with an internal response to this spinning globe and its unendingly creative energies. As a result of a respectful regard for other animals we may find that we are being led onto traveled ways that were once invisible to us, and in their deep alliance with natural forces we find a new depth in ourselves. This is the common ground for all living things, where migration has in it the blood of contact, the winds and waters of communication.

On that July week when I first saw the young alewives coming down through the outlet, the roads of Cape Cod were roaring and humming with cars. The tourist season had suddenly come to its height. The population of the Cape had jumped from 60,000 to 200,000 or more. There were new demands, new pressures in the air. This was the yearly coming on of an immense, expanding world, a migratory phenomenon in itself. Voices and prices were rising. Man's abundance vied with the natural summer.

It was a hot day, though it had started out cool in the early morning, with drifts of fog along the shore and patches of it through the inland hollows. I had followed the alewife fry down from the Herring Run to the shore road. They had become increasingly hard to find; but when I reached the slow waters of the channel at Paine's Creek I could see multitudes of them heading in the direction of the Bay. Farther on where the water ran out through the sands on the ebb tide there were groups of them moving with it like little clouds.

There were a few people walking on the flats in the distance where herring gulls were yelping and an occasional tern gave a light, harsh cry. An old panting setter dog lunged aimlessly across the sands, then splashed through the shallow waters of the creek at its outlet. On the beach a family crowd of bathers were listening to a portable radio that noised out the baseball scores. Some of them got up and saw to their children, or fell, sat down, or dove into the water at the edge of the sands. They sounded low, then high, like the gulls—"Stop it!" "Come on!" "Here, bunny" "Come back here!" "Jump in"—full of alarm, solicitude, friendliness, irritation, communality.

Back in the channel where the tiny fish, progeny of *Pomolobus pseudoharengus*, were swimming on in the brown water, a couple of growing, gawky children, a boy and a girl, half round, half lean, were pushing each other down, floundering and thrashing, while they laughed and threatened each other, completely oblivious of the great migration a few yards away. Or can anything be oblivious? I felt that I had come to the middle of things.

Also by

JOHN HAY

NATURE'S YEAR
THE GREAT BEACH

Available from Ballantine Books